GW00646645

First published in Great Britain in 1999 by VISION
Paperbacks, a division of Satin Publications Limited.

This book is copyright under the Berne Convention.
All rights reserved. No part of this publication may be
reproduced, stored in a retrieval system, or transmitted in
any form or by any means, electronic, mechanical,
photocopying, recording or otherwise, without prior
written permission of the publisher.

VISION Paperbacks,
a division of
Satin Publications Limited
20 Queen Anne Street
London W1M 0AY
E-mail: sheenadewan@compuserve.com

Design and layout: Justine Hounam
Printed and bound by The Bath Press

©1999 Ian Newton
ISBN: 1-901250-29-6

I would like to thank the following for their help:
John H. Garrod
Lisa Pearce
Malcolm M. Parkes
and many others

Everything in that moment came together – the factory gossip, the meeting in the park, the rumours about Prescott and Black – they all made a kind of sense. What was Terry asking me to get into? I walked back to the house in a haze. I could not start poking around in the affairs of the second most powerful man in the country and just walk away from it. And yet, you can't take on someone like him, no way. But then I thought, well, he can't be too good at hiding whatever it is he has been doing. World In Action aren't the only ones who know about it. A tea lady and half of a factory night-shift team seem to have heard that he could be up to something as well. And that settled it.

I walked in and my first instinct was to make a call, but then I remembered – no calls about this on my home telephone. I still could not believe it! I was high, amazed, depressed and puzzled, all at the same time. What was it he had done, if anything? I could not think, but my interest in all this was by now absolute. Yet, at the same time, I felt nauseous. What if he, or friends of his, were to find out that someone in the area had been doing a little snooping? Especially if he found out about my previous track record? A reporter from World In Action might be able to go around pointing the finger, but a night-shift worker who used to poke his nose into company's affairs for a hobby? Guess which one is most likely to be tolerated should he find out? Looking back now, I can see this as the moment I truly became part of the whole thing. I now knew who the story was about, finally, and I wanted to know more.

I was back at work the next day, and so I would discuss it with a couple of the others, hoping that maybe they could advise me, provided they would listen. I knew Joe would, and Gus, but as for the rest – forget it. They had told me the story to begin with, and their source I had laughed at, but it had turned out to be a damn sight more reliable than I credited.

DUSTBINGATE!

Chapter Six

Before going back to work, I decided to do some more snooping around. I figured I had about three or four hours to get some more information, and so it was back into my little book of numbers again. I had been told that some councillors had spoken to World In Action, but which ones? There were an awful lot of councillors in this neck of the woods, and so pinpointing who they were would take time. Luckily I had a contact that was worth trying. I had known a few of the councillors back in the days when I was on the fringes of Hull's local politics, but there was only the one I felt I could count on. Besides, he was the only one who would speak to me without thinking I was going to blackmail them.

Back in my little 'office' around the corner, I dialled the number and waited.

There was something deeply strange about standing in that phone box that I could not quite put my finger on – mind you, if that puddle in the corner was what I thought it was...

'Oh, hello.' It was the person I was after, and they sounded a little pensive. I do not know if it was because of why I was ringing or whether it's just my telephone manner, but when I say 'hello' to these people, it must invariably sound like: 'listen carefully, we have your daughter.' Still, I put it down to the fact that I had not rung in a while and pressed on.

We spoke about this and that before I cut to the chase. I asked him if it was true about local councillors having a chin-wag with World In Action, and he told me that it was. I asked him who and how many, and he told me that five councillors from different political parties had been interviewed.

I then asked how long the reporter had been in Hull, but he wasn't sure, although he guessed that he had been around one or two months. I then asked my sixty-four thousand dollar question

– what was the investigation all about? He let me know that it was about Prescott, and that was all he knew. I had heard this before, but somehow it seemed more concrete and real hearing it from him. I asked him for the councillors' names and he gave them.

Several of these I already had numbers for further conversations could be taken straight from the horse's mouths – hopefully. I thanked my gracious local politico for his time and, stepping out of my business headquarters, I ruminated on our brief conversation.

The World In Action reporter had obviously done a lot more work than most had given him credit for: five councillors interviewed, from different parties. I had the bones, but where was the meat? Every man and his dog, it seemed, knew it was about Prescott, but WHAT was it? It would soon be time for work, not that I cared. But it was certainly a grinding experience, going from phoning councillors to working the night shift for ten solid hours.

Back at home, I got ready to go to work and over and over in my mind, like a mantra, was the question: What did someone think Prescott had done? I was pulled out of my musings by my lass, who asked me if I had time to take the dog for a walk. I told her I was going to be late as it was. She was not happy and complained that the 'furry fuck' was not getting enough exercise. My suggestion that I take it to work and strap it to a conveyor belt seemed to fall on deaf ears.

'Now then, Ian, you look like how I feel,' said Joe as I plodded up to the canteen. This was the closest Joe could get to a 'How are you?' especially on the first day back on the job. Strangers hearing all this would think we hated each other, but it's just the way we speak to each other. Inside, the canteen was empty but for Gus and Malcolm. Gus had his feet on the table, and was staring off into space, obviously practising for later on, when he started work. Malcolm saw Joe and me stroll in.

'Lads, lads! Over here!' He waved excitedly.

Joe looked at Malcolm. 'Oh, there you are. Good job you waved – I wouldn't have spotted you in the crowd.' Joe grinned at me. He could be a sarcastic bastard when he felt like it and Malcolm was easy meat, always saying something, usually of a political nature, that could be torn to shreds. I got my coffee after Joe and we took our seats.

Gus sat up straight and yawned. 'Four days of this! I'm feeling well and truly fucked already,' he groaned. Malcolm turned to him. 'Christ, you've been here two friggin' minutes, Gus! Hey, did you here who's been down to Number Ten, then?' He looked straight at Joe as he spoke. 'Maggie Thatcher!'

'Fuckin' balls she has!' exclaimed Joe, 'No way has she been invited to Downing Street, you daft sod!' He shook his head as Malcolm carried on.

'It's true, Joe. What did I tell you, eh? Five minutes in power, and who's dunking digestives in a cup of tea? Only the very person Labour wanted out for the last eighteen years, that's who! All that time trying to get her out and the first person to wipe their feet on the doormat is the Iron Lady herself!' Malcolm was loving it. Joe glared daggers at him. 'Don't talk stupid, Malcolm,' was all he said. Malcolm sat back, basking in his little victory. Joe knew it was true, but he did not know what to say.

Gus suddenly broke the silence. 'Fuck this, it's no life, is it? I mean, who here has a good word to say about this place, eh? No-one, not even the bosses, I bet.' We all nodded in agreement.

'How long is it until shift starts?' enquired Joe, looking up at the clock.

'About twenty minutes,' I replied. 'Good, no need to rush then.' There was no chance of that happening. Not with us lot. We were the core of the night-shift. Apart from us, there was only Nick, Jeff the shift manager, a couple of shift fitters and two or three temporary workers.

These poor sods come in and go straight to work! They are so grateful to be in any kind of work that we see them as we are heading to the canteen, grafting away like robots. We are allowed to take breaks whenever we feel like it, which is damn near all the time, but these guys – they walk in and off they go! We would often discuss their ceaseless dedication and devotion to duty, usually whilst rolling fags and reading the paper during the fourth break of the night. Nick, however, was someone we were never keen to discuss. He was always there, always asking questions. We avoided him like the plague. He used to come with us on our breaks, but I guess the subtle hints that we did not want him around were eventually understood. I think it might have been when Gus told him to fuck off. All communications with him now were strictly about and during work, and that suited us.

'Hard at it as usual, I see', came a voice from behind me.

I turned around in my chair to see Harry standing in the doorway. 'All right, Harry! I thought you were on this shift next week. What happened?' I asked. He did not look best pleased. 'Rang us up, didn't they? Fucking had to come in – two of the temps are off sick or something'. He looked as happy to be there as the rest of us.

'They don't expect you to do the work of two, do they?' said Malcolm.

'I hope they don't expect me to do the work of one, I'm knackered,' came Harry's reply. 'Nah, another temp's here as well.' He came over and pulled up a chair.

We all knew each other so there was no need for introductions. We had all worked together and we trusted each other, which was fortunate in light of what I was about to tell them. 'Listen, while we're all here,' I began. There was no point trying to tippy-toe around the subject, it would only waste time.

'You know this thing about World In Action being in Hull, yeah?'

I looked around the room. Everyone was listening. That was a good sign, I thought, and so, with all eyes on me, I pressed on.

'Well, I found out something. I found out that they're looking into Prescott and Black.'

This had their attention. Usually, the big moment in a canteen conversation comes when someone declares they are off for a 'dump'.

Joe spoke first. 'Are you on about all that Keepmoat business?'

Joe was referring to a recent story in the papers about the rumours surrounding John Black's dealings with Keepmoat; a Doncaster-based property development company who were given the rights to build on land in the local area. What caused the upset was that usually when land is for sale, companies bid for it, but in this instance Keepmoat had allegedly bypassed the competitive tendering process and got the exclusive rights.

What made it worse was that the company was not even local. Questions were raised by the local press, namely why was the company given rights?

'Maybe,' I replied, 'But wouldn't you like to know exactly why they were here, and what they were interested in?' Joe stared at me.

'I doubt very much it had anything to do with Prescott,' he said, folding his arms. 'He's not one of your fuckin' fly by night shysters! He's a true Labour man, he's as straight as a die!'

Gus nodded his head. 'Too right. Anyroad, what are you doing? You're a factory worker, not a journalist! Christ!'

'You all know I used to be into politics, right?' I retorted, 'and that I've worked for newspapers before?'

'Yeah,' Gus answered, 'Fair enough, but why are you into this? Why tell us?'

I could see that they wanted answers. Only Harry had any idea about what I used to do, and so I had to step carefully. 'I'm just saying, wouldn't you like to find out?'

'For fuck's sake, what are you on about?' Joe was sitting bolt upright now. 'Prescott, doing dodgy deals? Listen, he's like me – hard left, OK? Just like my old man an' all. There's no shite about him. He's not one of your Blairite pansies, you know, he's a hard case. He doesn't have an alarm clock; his wife smacks him in the face with a baseball bat. When he farts, it registers on the Richter Scale in Tokyo. If a scab tried to drive through a picket line, he'd headbutt the fuckin' car off the road. Don't give me no crap about him, Ian.'

It didn't take an Einstein to figure that Joe was riled. I could see, throughout all this, Malcolm's eyes were lighting up, and I could sense what was going to happen.

Talk of politics, especially this kind of talk, was mother's milk to Malcolm.

'Face it,' he said, smile badly hidden, 'He's a politician! They're all at it! None of them know the meaning of the word honourable.'

Joe pushed a finger in Malcolm's face. 'About time you chipped in. I knew you'd be off on a rant. You're like fuckin' Citizen Smith or something, you are.' Joe was practically quivering with anger as he spoke. 'Armchair socialist, aren't you?' Malcolm shrugged. 'You can't understand it, can you Joe? Politicians are phoney, self-serving bastards. All of them. Why should he be any different?'

Joe leaned forward. 'He's all right, is Prescott!' he barked, and he brought his fist down on the table – hard.

'If you say so. But I'm telling you all, he's up to all sorts, you mark my words.'

'He's up to fuck all, you shit!' Harry looked at me. I knew what he was thinking – it was written all over his face – I could see him thinking, what the hell have we both started here? He's going to kill him! Joe hurtled on. It was like watching a car crash. You are near it, you can see it, but you cannot do anything to stop it.

'I know what you're like – you want to change the world, as long as you don't have to get up off your arse to do so. If there was a revolution, you'd be at home, watching it on the telly, a Socialist Worker in one hand, and a can of shandy in the other.' Joe's finger was now millimetres away from Malcolm's face.

Malcolm stayed silent.

'I don't know,' said Harry, 'It's like Question Time in here. Just let Ian have his say, all right? There's no need for punch-ups. Go on, Ian, continue.'

'I think we should have a look into what's going on. Do some digging. Are you all in?' Joe exhaled heavily, while Gus looked at me as if I had told them I was Princess Anastasia, heir to the Russian throne. 'What's the point? He's not up to fuck all, Ian, and since when did night-shift work and investigative journalism mix?' Joe asked.

'I'll tell you when,' Harry finished his coffee and stared at Joe. 'Since the moment I was born, I was told "Labour, Son, good old Labour, they'll see you right, don't you worry." And, do you know what? I believed it. Every word. My dad said it to me, my grand-dad said it, and all my life I've stuck by Labour.'

'Yeah. Too fuckin' right, as well,' Joe replied.

'OK. But just answer me one question, Joe – you an' all, Gus – what have you ever got out of it?'

'You don't support a party to make money!' Joe said.

'Fair comment,' Harry admitted, 'But aren't you tired of getting nothing at all from it?' He continued. 'I'm sick to death of having political principles when the politicians don't have them! Let's take a pop at them! If anyone is up to anything, then let's find out! I'm tired of all this crap! I'm not scared, are you?' Everyone shook their heads. Harry's speech seemed to do the trick.

'OK, what's the plan?' Joe said.

'Well, I thought that one of us should approach the World In Action reporter,' I replied.

'It better not be Malcolm who goes,' Gus laughed, 'he'll be telling the poor bastard all about Hull's political links with Idi Amin.' 'Look,' I said, 'There's only one fair way of doing it. We'll draw straws.' I got up and went over to the coffee machine. There was always a little pot of straws next to it for soft drinks. I took one, broke it in half as best I could and put it in the palm of my hand along with four others.

I walked up to the table. 'Take one,' I said simply.

Harry went first, then Gus, followed by Joe and then Malcolm.

They all held their straws up. I opened my fist. There, in the palm of my hand, was the broken straw. 'Fucking typical,' I gasped.

'I'm glad,' Gus said, slinging his straw over his shoulder. 'No offence, like.'

'None taken,' I said, still looking at my palm.

'What are you going to do, Ian?' asked Malcolm.

'I'm going to do what I said: go see the World In Action guy.'

Gus stood up. 'When are you off?'

'First day off, I suppose. I'll let you all know how I get on.'

Gus headed for the door. 'Don't worry, we can wait.' And off he strolled.

Everyone filed out, until it was just Harry and myself. As I went through the door, he put his arm in the way, blocking the door.

'Are you thinking what I'm thinking?' was all he said.

'What are you on about?' I asked him.

'If there *is* a story going on, what then? Give it to him?' He moved his arm.

'I guess so, why?' I answered.

'Ian,' Harry said slowly, 'There's money to be made here.'

He was right. I had not thought about it before, but he was absolutely right. 'Why let someone else make all the money? We could sell the story ourselves, make a fortune. If it's big enough, of course. We can do it. Remember, when we took on one of the biggest companies in the world, no-one could touch us! This is smaller if anything, but there's cash here, trust me. I meant what I said, Ian, I'm not scared.'

'Neither am I,' I replied, 'Prescott is just a man.'

I knew what he was talking about. We had politically 'scammed' a huge company in the past, and they had not known what had hit them.

The company had been about to make some of us redundant. It did not seem to matter to this company that only months earlier they had enticed many of us away from safe well-paid jobs, with their impressive adverts of job security and promotion. Well, it seemed they had miscalculated, and it was to be 'Mr Joe Ordinary' who was to be made to pay for their mistakes by being kicked out on his arse and onto the dole queue. The union at this company was about as useful as a one-legged man at an arse-kicking competition. So outside the company, our little group decided to engage the company in a 'dialogue' of sorts. It involved one of the most bizarre political scams we had ever pulled. By the time we had finished the company had been totally confused and compromised. Of those chosen on the initial list to be made redundant, only three were made redundant. The important part of the trick had worked, company psychology, of sorts, had been turned on the company. Most ordinary people have a tendency to think in straight lines, the issues to them are black and white, and of course they rarely are.

Harry walked out the doorway. He turned around. 'Don't tell the others, at least not yet. They'll only start champing at the bit. You and me, Ian, we've had nothing but heartache when it comes to politics! Don't fumble the ball, my friend,' he smiled, 'and it could be the factory today, Acapulco tomorrow!'

He strode off to the shop floor.

He was right: telling the others money could be made would only result in a major headache. Besides, I knew Gus would not hang around. I looked at him when we had to pull straws – he was scared shitless. He would be gone soon, I could feel it.

Now, I know what you are thinking; why ask them to pull straws when they would most probably have cocked the whole thing up a treat? Here is the reason – it was a simple test of faith. Thank God I got the short straw. In case you are wondering, it was pure coincidence.

I could see that things had begun to snowball. To lose control now would have been a great shame, especially when I felt so close to finding out the truth.

Chapter Seven

The night wore on as slowly as it always did, only this time I had the added bonus of wondering if Gus would grass me up for trying to subvert the minds of my fellow workers. Was it my overactive imagination, or was he avoiding me?

The realisation that Gus was obviously not interested was sinking in. I liked Gus, he was a good guy, but the look in his eyes as I spoke about the whole deal spoke volumes: I was hoping for 'count me in!' Instead I got 'count me out' – with a side order of 'fuck you and the horse you rode in on.'

Gus was an ordinary working man, and ordinary working men have but one certainty in life – to get a job, do that job and be grateful; don't do anything to jeopardise it. Now, even Gus knew that of all the things you can do to potentially lose your job, looking into the affairs of the Deputy Prime Minister is pretty high on the 'Don't you even think about it' list. I'm not one for getting carried away, but I couldn't help but worry that Gus might do a 'Nick' on us, and tell on us for 'political activism', or whatever you want to call it.

I did not think the local union boys would descend on us from a great height, crying 'My god! You're all a bunch of communist bastards!' for one second. But I did not want to come to work and find that the Union knew what we were up to. Which is why I wanted to talk to Gus, persuade him that jawing with anyone about this would be a daft idea. It was easier said than done as I could not find the bastard anywhere.

You would think that, with us just being a small group, there would be no problems in contacting one another. Well, not tonight, it seemed. I went to the canteen, he had already left; I went back to the machines, he was having a piss, and so on.

No-one else let on about anything all night, and for that I was grateful. Loose lips sink ships and in the back of my mind, growing bigger every minute, was the image of Gus getting ready to fire one big mother-fucking torpedo.

Finally, our paths crossed. Outside the canteen, I spotted him, heading towards the door. I followed him inside and, seeing that the place was empty, I thought I would get it all off my chest.

I crept up behind him, real easy, like. It did not occur to me at the time that it was not the wisest thing to do, creeping up on a hard-case who has a cup of boiling hot coffee in his hand, but I wasn't thinking about that; I was thinking, 'what have you been saying?'

'All right, Gus?' I said, slapping him on the back and giving him my most sincere smile. He turned slowly, pocketing his change from the coffee machine as he did so.

His face was set.

'Oh, Ian,' he replied, 'What's the problem?' He moved away from me and went to one of the tables, all stains and crushed cups. I would have felt more welcome if I'd been a rapper at a Ku Klux Klan rally. He sat down, and I joined him.

'You don't seem very happy tonight, Gus,' I asked. He looked down into his cup. 'Nah, I'm all right.' I knew he wasn't, he was pretty far from all right; normally Gus would sit down, take a sip of his coffee and flap his gums about anything and everything to whoever was in listening distance. He was not fooling anyone, something had pissed the guy off, and there were no prizes for guessing who.

I wanted to know so badly if he had talked. I was angry, not at him, but at myself; angry because I'd told him something I should-n't, and that if he had gone to the Union to tell 'Them who must be obeyed' then I would look like an idiot. He sat quietly, looking at the ceiling, at the door – anywhere but at me.

'Gus... How should I put this? Have you told anybody anything?

Have you? You're not happy about it are you?'

Gus made eye contact. 'Not happy about what?'

'I think you know what I'm on about,' I said. He just stared out of the window, silent again. I leaned over the table. 'Gus, what's up? Why are you so off with me?'

'Because.' He pushed his coffee cup to one side, and got up out of his chair.

I got up, too, sensing that if I wanted any answers I'd better make my move now.

'Hang on, Gus. Why don't you want in?'

'Why don't I want in?' He looked me straight in the eyes. He made it sound so incredulous, so stupid, as if I had asked him why he didn't want to dip his dick in hot chip fat. He turned around and began to walk back to the shop floor.

I didn't want to talk about it in front of the others – I could handle a slanging match, but I would prefer it to be without an audience. I walked behind him, talking all the way.

'Gus, why don't you want in? What's up? If you don't want to have anything to do with it, fair enough, but at least tell me why.' Gus stopped still in his tracks. I honestly thought he was going to spin around and punch me. I can recall thinking, Oh fuck, please Gus, not the face.

'I think,' he stopped, as if gathering up his thoughts, 'I think the whole thing is really stupid, Ian. World In Action? Fuckin' journalists. Are you pulling my pud or what?' He rolled his huge hands into fists. 'I don't know what you're playing at, but I'm having nothing to do with it. Got that, Ian? I don't know what you think you're going to do, anyway. You can't take on the Deputy Prime minister, you crazy bastard!'

'Did I say I was?' I interrupted, 'But at the same time he does not scare me either.'

'You work in a factory!' was his reply, and with that, he was on his way back to the shop floor.

I don't know what was stronger in my mind at that moment in time: bewilderment at Gus's attitude, or gratefulness that he had left me with all my teeth intact.

I realised then and there that I had misjudged the situation, and misjudged it badly. We should never in a million years have involved someone like Gus. To Gus, politicians were like deities, icons. They were untouchable.

Gus hit the nail on the head in a big way when he said, 'You work in a factory!' To him, we were all just factory workers, we should know our place. I knew then and there that if the rest of us were to continue, I would have to do something pretty quickly, in case he said something to the union. Walking back onto the shop floor, I saw Joe and Harry, one at each end of a machine, and looking suitably industrious. Gus was to the left of Harry, stand-ing stock still and staring down at the floor. A second later, Malcolm wandered into view. Good, I thought, get them all togeth-er in one fell swoop and save my ass by telling them the whole thing is over.

As I approached Harry, the others seemed to instinctively wander over as well.

Out the corner of my eye, I saw Gus bring up the rear, slowly plodding across the floor.

Harry cocked an eyebrow. 'What's the problem?' he asked, as the machines hissed and juddered in the background. We all stood around in a semi-circle. I looked at Gus, who for the first time that night seemed interested in something.

'Lads, I've been thinking. This whole World In Action thing...'

'Yeah? Go on', Joe said, 'what about it?'

'Well, I've been thinking, like, and well, I reckon we should just forget the whole thing. You know, leave it alone.' I looked up to see some pretty puzzled faces staring back at me. 'But,' Malcolm gasped, 'you were all for it before!' He almost looked hurt.

'For fuck's sake, Ian, make up your mind,' said Joe, shaking his head. 'A few hours ago, we were all set, ready to go, and now you're knocking it on the head?'

'What's brought this on? What made you change your mind?' inquired Harry.

I did not look at Gus. 'We can't do fuck all, can we? I mean, let's face reality. We're a bunch of factory workers, for Christ's sake! What can we do?'

Malcolm straightened himself up. 'I'm not a factory worker,' he said, indignantly.

'Oh no?' said Joe, 'Then what are you doing here, you soft shit? If you're not a factory worker then I suggest you leave because you're due at work in about four hours.'

Malcolm, as ever, did not respond to Joe. 'I've got a degree,' he continued, 'I won't be here much longer, you know, I'm looking for proper work,' and with that he turned around and went back to his machine.

'I think you should look a bit harder mate,' Joe called after him, 'you've been here two years!' Malcolm did not hear him, the machines were roaring away now and I felt I had done what needed to be done.

'You all right there, Gus?' asked Harry, noticing his silence. 'You're a bit on the quiet side tonight. Everything OK?' Gus nodded. Joe shrugged his shoulders. 'Well, if that's that, then fair enough. Back to work, I suppose.' He stretched his arms up in the air and yawned. 'Fuckin' factory work!' he laughed, and off he strode, back to the grindstone.

Harry shot me a look I couldn't quite decipher and then he too was gone. It was just Gus and myself, and I would probably have to do the talking for both of us.

'I'm sorry about all this, Gus,' I said.

'Was all that on my behalf?' he replied.

'As if I would!' I smiled. 'Nah, you made me see sense. All that stuff about World In Action. It was all just hot air, big ideas.' I patted Gus on the back. 'Forget all about it, yeah? I'm all talk.'

He actually looked relieved when I said this. He smiled, as if a great weight had been lifted from his shoulders, and he practically skipped away to the canteen.

I went over to find Harry, who was sitting down in a plastic chair he'd grabbed from the canteen. He gave a nod of the head as I spotted him.

'Any more bright ideas, then?' he said, rocking back on the chair's legs.

'What's wrong with the one we've already got?' I said, keeping watch for Gus's imminent return.

Harry understood, and leapt to his feet, an astonished expression on his face. 'You crafty bastard!' he laughed. 'I should have known you wouldn't flush it down the pan!'

'Shh! Keep it down! I said all that in front of Gus so he would not grass us up! Listen, tell Joe and Malcolm when you've got time and the coast is clear, OK? We'll have to keep it outside the factory from now on. We'll have to find somewhere.'

'Whereabouts?' Harry asked. 'Your house?'

'Are you kidding me? If my lass saw you lot anywhere near my street, let alone house she'd have kittens. No, we'll have to meet at a pub or something.'

'Have you got anywhere in mind?'

'Yeah, I have as a matter of fact, and it's perfect.'

And with that we were down to four. Gus was out. As my mind

ticked over the rest of that night, I decided we would not be four
for very long.

DUSTBINGATE!

Chapter Eight

Jim was an old acquaintance from the days when I was interested in what was happening on the local political scene. He knew me as a fervent believer in the goodness of socialism and so naturally took the piss something chronic.

We both had interests in politics; he was always arguing the toss. Like all disruptive political animals, though, he was put down – the killer blow being a rather unfortunate skirmish, not relevant to this story, which was ever more referred to as the 'union set-up'. He became very embittered and slipped from sight.

'Ian! You bastard!' he yelled down the phone. Time had mellowed him, it seemed.

'Now then, fella,' I said, hoping he was joking with me. 'What've you been up to, eh? Still fighting for the working man's rights?'

'Not quite,' he replied, his voice dropping a gear. 'The working man can fuck right off. I look after myself now.'

'Spoken like a true cynical bastard. You'd almost think you worked nights.'

'I do.'

'Oh, fuck. Sorry to hear that.'

'Don't upset yourself,' he said, 'It's not your fault. So, what can I do you for?'

I asked him when he was free and luckily one of his days off coincided with one of mine, so we arranged to meet. The gap left by Gus was now filled and things seemed to be moving apace. However, I knew that in terms of actually finding anything, we had not even begun; but I was hoping my other new-found friend could help me with that.

'It's your friend from Hull,' I said, as the call to World In Action was put through.

'I didn't expect to hear from you again,' said the voice.

'No?' I replied, 'Well, believe me, I'm on the level here. I want to help you.'

'Why?'

'For me,' I said, 'and the people I work with, it's very interesting to us. We want to help, but if we do, don't ever mention us, not for our sakes, but for the people around us.' Okay, it wasn't the most original piece of dialogue, but it had to sound earnest and enigmatic. Besides, it seemed to do the trick. He was intrigued, even more so when I gave him my home telephone number and asked him to ring me back there.

The reason I gave him my number was simple – I'd found that to get anywhere with a journalist, you had to show a bit of trust. You give them something, and, hopefully, they'll give you more in return.

I told him to give me fifteen minutes and then ring me back. He did not ask why I wanted the time, and I was glad for that. 'Ooh, I'll need fifteen minutes to get home from the phone box,' would not exactly instill him with faith.

About twelve minutes after I got home, the phone rang. I gave him my real name, as I decided that the name 'Stephen' would only be used sparingly. I wanted to be absolutely straight with this guy, and so, again, a show of faith was called for. I had his real name, so he should have mine.

He did not mince his words in this brief conversation.

'Did you know Prescott got his house for twenty eight thousand pounds?' he asked.

'What?' This was news to me; I had seen Prescott's house. Getting that for twenty eight thousand pounds seemed a bit low, but at that point I could not relate a price to values at the time he had moved in.

'How did you manage to find that out?' I enquired.

'It's in his biography. Haven't you read it? It says he got "a bit of a bargain."'

'I'll fuckin' say! Have you seen the size of his house? It's massive! A bit of a bargain? Where did he get it from? I've got a spare fiver and I could do with a new washing machine.'

'The book says it was a former Salvation Army hostel.' There was a slight pause in the flow of conversation and I took that to mean it was time for me to give. At the time, I did not think I was saying much, but the reaction I got was surprising, to say the least.

'There's two bungalows on the back of Prescott's house,' I began. And finished, because the World In Action man jumped in.

'Since when?' he exclaimed, his voice rising.

'Since he got the planning permission a few years ago. Actually, now that I think about it, there was the most almighty stink at the time, but I think it was just some of you media people having a pop at him,' I said, sarcastically.

'Oh, of course.'

I had taken no notice at the time, but Nick had mentioned the bungalows to us.

He lived near them, and his ears and eyes were evidently as big as his mouth. He said one night in the canteen: 'There's two little bungalows around the corner from me. You wanna see 'em! They're like little Kensington Palaces! They stick out like a couple of hard-ons in a monk's choir!'

I was ruminating on what a small world it was when the World In Action man spoke again.

'I'm sure you've heard of...'

He mentioned the name of a local club. I had heard of it, but then he asked me if I knew anything about any grants the club had associated with it. I told him that I hadn't. 'It's news to me,' I said, to which he replied, 'Can you find out?'

'I doubt it,' Where did you get the info about the grants, anyway?'

'Someone told me, who, bizarrely, I can't speak to anymore.' he said. It was his turn to be enigmatic, and although I had a pretty good idea who he was talking about, I was not sure. Then he asked me if I could find anything on these grants. I told him I couldn't – but I knew a man who could.

By the end of the conversation, we had decided to meet and talk face to face. I felt I had gained his trust now, and that perhaps we could work together and find out exactly what it was he was looking into. He remained cagey about specifics, and I did not want to blow it by asking him out right. When the time was right, he would tell me, and no doubt ask what my interest was. I was sure of it.

Next, I called Dan, who was an old friend of mine. Dan had just lost his job, and had been blacklisted for his political beliefs. He was now on the dole, and it occurred to me to ask him to come along to our little booze up. He was in, the phone being picked up after just two rings.

'Hello?' He sounded depressed.

'Dan, it's Ian. How are you?'

'I'm on the dole, Ian. Take a wild guess.'

'Are you doing anything Thursday?' I asked.

'Do you mean before or after the Opera? Ian, are you taking the piss out of me?'

'No, mate! I'm sorry. Look, come out for a drink. I'm off out on the piss with a few of the lads from work, and I think you should come along. How about it?' Since Dan had lost his job he had withdrawn from the world somewhat. I never saw him anymore, and nobody liked a pint more than Dan.

'Oh, all right. Where are we meeting? What time?'

I filled him in on the details, and he said he would be there. There were now six of us: Joe, Malcolm, Harry, Jim, Dan and myself. No Gus. At least, I was hoping there would be no Gus. Trying to keep a piss-up secret from Gus was like trying to find a fart in a thunderstorm – impossible. If he did turn up, then I would have to shelve the plans I had for the night, which was something I really did not want to have to do.

Tonight the plan of action was being unveiled.

We were meeting at a pub called The Duke Of York, in a place called Sutton, on the outskirts of Hull. There were three reasons for meeting there: one, it was known to us all; two, it was a very quiet pub, so we could talk in peace; and three, it was a stone's throw from the home of a certain Deputy Prime Minister. The irony of this did not escape us.

Joe was already there when I arrived, and I saw him sitting by the window looking more pensive than I had ever seen him before. He was nursing a pint and staring off into space, oblivious to the world.

'Fuckin' hell, Joe, how many have you had?' I asked, as I went to the bar and ordered myself a drink. He looked up, almost in a trance.

'Anyone else with you?' he said, standing up and finishing off his drink.

'No, looks like we're the first ones here,' I replied.

He was nervous about something, I could see it. He stood close to me and almost whispered what he had to say.

'Ian, I'm off.' He slammed the empty pint glass onto the counter.

'What?' This was not like Joe. We were in a pub, for God's sake. 'How long have you been here?' Normally, he would be trying to light one of his farts by now, and here he is about to bail out of a drinking session before it's even started. 'What's up with you, mate?' I asked.

'I don't want this.'

'Don't want what?'

'This. The meetings, the drama. If word got out, it could get a bit hairy.'

'Easy, mate. What are you worried about?' He looked around the pub. 'Ian, this isn't having a fag break when you shouldn't, you know. This is serious! I don't fancy flying off the Humber Bridge at midnight in concrete wellies.'

'That's a bit on the hysterical side, isn't it? We're talking about the Labour Party here, not the Mafia.' I felt despondent: first Gus, now Joe – it was like 'Invasion of The Body Snatchers'.

Everyone was talking the talk, but when it came to walking the walk, suddenly, their legs did not work. He pulled out his car keys and shrugged.

'I'll help you, OK? Ask me to do something, I'll do it; only leave me in the shadows, all right? If you make any cash, slip me a few notes in a brown paper bag.'

'Fair enough,' I sighed. I knew what he meant, and at least it wasn't as bad as Gus's little song and dance. I smiled at Joe.

'No worries, fella. Cheers!' I held up my drink.

'Cheers, Ian. Good luck.' He turned and left.

I took my seat in a corner. It was the quietest place the pub had, as well as the most private. It wasn't like most other pubs; it was civilised. If you spilt someone's pint in here, you would not be hit with a dry cleaning bill; and having both ears pierced did not get you beaten up for being gay. I sat facing the door, and, half way through my pint, Dan walked in.

'Evening, Ian. My, what a swinging party.' He stared at the empty chairs next to me. After getting himself a drink he sat down.

'Where's everyone else, then?' he asked. A fair enough question, really.

'They'll be here, don't worry. No way will any of them miss a piss-up.'

As if on cue, in walked Malcolm, closely followed by Harry. Drinks in hand, they took their seats, and, a brief introduction later, we were all old buddies. Five minutes later, we were joined by Jim. Time for business, I thought, but no, everyone wanted to get pissed.

I should have told them why we were meeting, but then I thought no, I'd rather tell them when they were drunk.

I have to hand it to Malcolm; he went for nearly three minutes before mentioning politics. Things got loud between Malcolm and Jim, who did not exactly hit it off. They weren't too loud, but it was probably the closest that this quiet pub had ever come to a brawl, and the barman soon started to watch us. As the empty pint glasses mounted up, and the rest of us tried to discuss other topics, those two went at it hammer and tongs.

'Will you two please give it a rest? It's like being out on the piss with Karl Marx,' said Harry rising to get another round in. I could see Dan becoming more and more fed up with the proceedings.

'How long have we been here?' he asked, not hiding his boredom.

'Hang on.' I looked at my watch. 'Christ, only an hour and half.'

'If these two keep on about revolutions, I'm gonna fuck off,' he whispered.

There was no argument from me. I saw Harry's face as he returned with the drinks and I could see he was of the same mind.

' Let me ask you something, Malcolm,' said Jim, in mid-flow, 'do you believe that the only thing stopping the working classes taking over the country is their inability to group together?'

'Too right, I do,' came Malcolm's reply. He barely noticed Harry handing him a pint as he hit his stride once more.

'We are just one big riot away from revolution.'

Jim almost choked on his pint. 'Fuck off out of it!' He turned to the rest of us.

'Is this guy for real?' he said. 'You, fella, are nothing more than a watered down Lenin in a chunky sweater.'

Malcolm looked enraged. I don't know if it was the Lenin bit that upset the most, although my money was on the insult to his jumper.

We were about to go another five rounds of topical debate, when I stepped in.

'Lads, calm down, for fuck's sake! If I wanted to listen to this crap I'd watch Question time, all right?' The two of them stared at me, angry that I'd spoiled their fun, no doubt. I was a little pissed off with this, I hadn't asked Jim along to bait Malcolm into a row, and Dan looked set to leave – and I would not have blamed him.

Harry seemed happy enough, though, sitting and sipping at his pint, letting the discussion rage on around him. Then he spoke.

'I'm starving,' he said. He might not have said much that night, but when he did, boy, was it worth waiting for.

'Look, we'll go get something in a minute,' I snapped. I was becoming exasperated by this point. Everything had gone wrong: Joe going AWOL, Jim and Malcolm rowing like two first year politics students, and now Harry, demanding his supper.

I had to tell them why we were here now, or else the whole thing would be a total washout. I had their attention, so I continued.

'There's a reason I wanted us all to meet,' I said.

'Aye, and here it is!' grinned Jim, lifting aloft his pint.

'Not the beer,' I said, 'Prescott.'

With that, the group went quiet. I had explained only in very vague detail this whole saga to Jim and Dan on the phone, but they looked completely dumbstruck when I said his name.

'Prescott?' Dan repeated.

'Yeah,' I replied. 'Can I ask you all a question?' No answer, so I did.

'We all have one thing in common, us five...'

'Aye, and here it is!,' said Jim, hoisting up his glass again.

'Change the record, Jim! No, it's not that. Dan, you lost your job because you spoke up for your politics; Jim, you've been blacklisted; Harry, the same; me, I've been shafted, too. Just one question: Aren't you sick of being fucked over?' With this, everyone went silent.

'All this sleaze stuff at the council, I just want to sort out the fact from the fiction, find out what's going on.' Still silence. 'I'm not talking about giving what we find away to the press, or whatever. I'm talking about making a shit load of money so we can all get out of the ruts we're in, maybe even open that newspaper you've always been on about, Dan. Do something constructive.' Dan nodded to himself. So did the rest, as what I said sank in. Then Malcolm spoke up.

'Hey,' he said slowly, 'If we find something real big, it could bring down the government!' With that, the group went silent again.

Harry looked lost in thought, then: 'Does anyone want a bag of pork scratchings?' Just then, an idea hit me. I got up, finished my pint, and said: 'Come on.' I headed for the door. Harry jumped up, looking a little worse for wear.

'Are we off to the chippy?' he asked, hopefully.

'Just come on, all of you,' I ordered.

Outside, it was dark, and the wind was getting up. 'Ian, where are we going?' asked Malcolm.

'I want to show you something,' I said, but as I walked I got the distinct impression I was alone. I turned around to find that I was. As I looked off into the distance, I saw the four of them running out of the Chinese take away and heading towards me.

They were all eating trays of chips. Typical, the finest cuisine in the world, and not only do they come back with fried spuds, but they didn't bring any for me.

'Where are we off?' Jim asked, in between mouthfuls.

'I want to show you a couple of bungalows,' I said, bracing myself against the wind.

'My, you certainly know how to show a boy a good time,' said Dan.

'It's like being in charge of a chimp's tea party,' I remarked, watching the four of them chomp away at their food.

Then there was the most almighty crash, and I spun on my heels to see Jim flat on his back, and yelling to the sky in pain.

'What happened?' I shouted, while the rest of them, as compassionate as ever, roared with laughter at the hapless Jim, who was rolling around on the pavement squealing in agony.

'Ah, my back! Oh fuck!' He was helped up by Malcolm and Harry, who had raced to his aid immediately – after finishing off their chips. Jim panted out his words 'Fuckin' empty tray,' and everyone looked at Dan, who was still licking his hands clean.

As we rounded the corner, we found ourselves walking past the home of the Deputy Prime Minister himself, and I noticed that there was no Jim. As I turned around I could make out his silhouette standing and facing the side of Mr Prescott's privet hedge. I was just about to ask him what he was doing, when he started to giggle. He was trying to peek through it.

'Hey,' he shouted to us. 'I think I can see his dustbin!'

'For fuck's sake!' I hissed, 'Do you know who's behind that hedge? The secret service! Now shift it, before you get your helmet shot off!'

'Hang on then,' he replied. 'I need to drain the python.'

Harry was up ahead in front, and seemingly eager to get a look at these bungalows. Malcolm came up to me. 'What's the big story with these bungalows, again?' he asked me, his words ever so slightly slurred.

'Wait until you see them,' was all I said, and moments later, we were there – Ings Road Estate, Balham Avenue. The street was very quiet, and as we approached I told everyone to keep the noise down.

'What's the big deal?' Dan said, staring at the two buildings.

'That used to be the back of Prescott's garden,' was my reply. 'Selling a piece of land with planning permission included is worth its weight in gold.'

Dan looked at the bungalows again, then at me. 'Why is he selling land?' He stepped forward in order to get a better look at them.

The two bungalows did not seem to fit in with the surrounding area, which was a grey and sterile council estate. Just painting your house a different colour on the estate needed council approval, and I should know; I used to live there.

'He certainly has taste,' Dan remarked.

'He sure does,' replied Malcolm.

We all turned away and headed back out onto the road. It was freezing, and as we walked I spoke.

'All I'm saying is this. We've all got connections, haven't we? We've got the Deputy Prime Minister on our doorstep! The

DUSTBINGATE!

Council's in turmoil over this sleaze shit. We can all do 'the business', one way or another, can't we? Only this time, it's different. This time, it's for us. Look at it like this: the Government likes private/public partnerships, doesn't it? Well, we're doing just that, we're going into partnership with the Government.' We all stopped dead in our tracks. We looked at each other, and Dan started to laugh, then Malcolm, and suddenly, we were all laughing, the sound being blown away on the wind.

Chapter Nine

I replayed the events of last night's revelries in my head as I woke up the next morning. I think I would have stayed in bed had it not been for the dog howling its head off at the foot of the bed. The last thing I wanted to do was take the dog for a walk; I wanted to have some breakfast and start ringing around. My head was pounding, and I got out of bed real slow, and opened the bedroom door. 'Go on,' I said, 'Go downstairs, I'll take you for a walk in a minute.' The dog looked up at me, cocked its head, and trotted off out of the room.

The dog put me in a shitty mood, and thinking about last night did not improve things. The previous night I had been after ideas and input, but what I got was someone going 'arse over tit' and nearly breaking his back, a potential indecent exposure court appearance, and the offer of a bag of pork scratchings.

As I wandered down stairs, I thought about the next plan of action. I hadn't expected everyone getting pissed up and pratting about like goons. No, if you want something doing, do it yourself, and that was exactly what I was going to spend the day doing – as soon as I had walked the dog.

One hour later and I was on the telephone. My plan only to ring from the public phone box around the corner had soon gone out of the window. This was primarily because I had to give the journalist from World In Action my home phone number, although the foul smell in the phone box was a contributing factor.

I rang a contact I had at the council offices at Beverley, which was just outside Hull. There would be planning files at this office, pertaining to the 'club' the World in Action reporter spoke of. These files would have all kinds of information that would assist the investigation; accountants' telephone numbers; the agent's address; designer's plans – all things that can be exploited for further leads. The problem was that copies cost a pound a page at the offices. I don't want to give any details about my contact there, but he was delighted to hear from me, asking him to do something that could be seriously compromise his job. He was even happier when he found the file and told me that it was 'as fat as a phone directory.'

'What is it exactly you're after?' he asked.

'Anything on grants,' I answered.

'Give me a couple of days.' I wasn't happy about the waiting time, but knowing I had no choice in the matter, I agreed. I guess I just wanted to find out what was in that file.

Nearly an hour later, the phone rang. 'Guess what I've found?' It was my friend from the Council Offices. I could not believe it! 'You said two days, you sod!'

'Yeah, I know, but you got me curious, so I had a good look, and I've found something straight off.'

'What?'

'Well,' he said, 'There's a two page letter from someone at [the club] addressed to the planning office which mentions employment grants, and a grant from the Department of the Environment in Sheffield, relating to unemployed people. To be honest, I haven't really had time to read them properly.' He was still talking, but I wasn't listening. A light bulb had gone on in my mind.

I said, 'I'll ring you back in ten minutes' and I put the phone down, only to pick it straight back up again to call World In Action.

'Employment grants?' I simply said.

There was silence on the other end of the line. World In Action had only mentioned 'grants' to me and I knew I had found what I had found what he was looking for.

'When can I see them?' he asked.

'When we meet you'll know everything I do.' He asked me to keep him updated and told me to reverse the charges if I had to.

I wish I'd thought of that. I thanked him, and before he hung up, he said, 'read Prescott's biography. You might find out something.' I told him I would, and I then called back my friend at the Council offices.

I arranged to get copies of what we needed and he said that would be no problem. I rang off, feeling happy although we had a long way to go, I had the first piece of substantial information in the bag, and it was now the others' turns. Not wanting another session in the pub, I decided to get on the phone to Dan.

I told him what I had, and he sounded amazed. I think deep down he thought the whole thing was just so much bullshit, but when I told him about ringing World In Action he seemed to sit up and take notice. 'Are you doing anything this afternoon?' I said.

'Don't start that again, Ian,' he growled.

'We've got a job needs doing, so listen...' I told him that he was to go and look at planning precedents and applications in the vicinity of Salthouse Road, near John Prescott's house. Dan replied; 'John Prescott must have bought land off the council, you know, in order to get access to Balham Avenue.'

'Correct,' I replied, 'and that means there must be documents at the Council on the transfer of land. I also want you to go to the Register of Electors, and find out who lived at Prescott's house before he did. If you're not too busy, that is.'

'Fuck off!' he said, adding, 'Just you leave it to me,' I remembered that I wasn't the only one who knew people. I got up and made myself a cup of tea, the dog loyally following me to the kitchen. I looked down at the dog, and thought about how loving, loyal and unconditional it was. It never asked for anything from me, save the occasional walk and its food. For a second, I almost admired its blind sense of loyalty. I used to be like that when it came to politics. But not anymore, though.

'Uh? Hello?'

'Christ, you sound like you've just been exhumed,' I said.

'Oh, Ian, all right?' replied Malcolm, half-asleep. 'I've not been sleeping too well. Woman troubles – you know how it is.' I did, but I didn't want to know about it just then, so I gave him his task: to pull some documents from Land Registry.

'Aw, Ian, that costs money, you know,' he moaned.

'It's only four pounds a pop, that's all! Oh, and get me John Black's documents as well.' Malcolm went into spasm.

'You what? That's eight quid!' 'I know. I'm really good at maths. Look, eight quid is fuck all, all right? You'll just have to go without a couple of new jumpers for a while, that's all.' 'I bet no-one else is having to pay out any money,' he continued.

'Fuckin' hell, Malcolm, I'll give you the money myself. And, by the way, use the name 'Stephen' when you fill in the receipt at the Land Registry, OK?'

'OK,' came the somewhat sheepish reply, 'I'll do it. When do you want them for?' We arranged to meet at the Duke of York again, with me telling Dan, Jim and Harry. I had yet to dish out tasks to the latter two and, with the other night's fun and games still very much in my head, I wondered whether I should bother at all. I decided that we needed all the help possible, so I rang Harry. I filled him in on what was happening, and then asked him if we could expect a repeat performance. He was in an unapologetic mood.

'Hey, I'm not the one who whipped out his shlong and pissed all over a hedge, remember?' He had a point.

'All right, forget all about that. Listen up, this is your part of the plan.' Harry listened, understood. He was to dip into the Council network and speak to the councillors who spoke to World In Action. I gave him the names that I had, and told him to get searching. Believe it or not, Harry can be a very clever man when the mood takes him, and I was hoping he would do the business. I asked him to ring Jim and tell him to turn up.

'Aren't you going to give him anything to do?' he asked.

'Yeah,' I said, 'I thought he could water my back garden. Now fuck off and get going, we haven't got forever on this.'

Actually, Harry had made a very good point: what was Jim going to do? I guessed I'd have to think that one over. I did not want to piss the guy off; or else he might piss on me.

That afternoon, a source very close to Prescott got a telephone call. There was nothing strange about that; this person got dozens of them a week, possibly a day. This one particular caller, however, was not all he seemed.

Being able to question someone in Prescott's inner circle was a valuable asset. But how does one build a rapport? In my experience, you cannot ring them up and ask 'What's been going on?' Over the course of days, weeks, months, you ring up and talk bullshit and then you say 'what's been going on?' Not from a suspicious, curious point of view, but from a friendly, concerned one. And you never ring up as yourself. You ring as someone who the source will say practically anything to, without thinking twice about it.

Just such a person stepped into the fray. He was eighty-two, hard of hearing, had a leaky toilet that he could not get fixed and had trouble with his legs. Enter the pensioner. Enter the fictional character Albert Gunner.

Albert is a Labour man, through and through, and he was trying to get his bungalow toilet fixed up. So he rang the source close to Prescott.

'Hello?' says the source.

'Yes, hello?' comes the croaky old voice, 'Can I speak to some-one about my toilet, please?' The source breathes a deep sigh.

'Now then, Albert old son, how are you today?' the source says.

'Oh, you know, sir, not too bad, I can't feel my legs at the moment, you know, but apart from that, I'm not too bad, sir.'

'I'm glad to hear it, Albert. Now, what can I do you for?'

'Well, sir, it's about my toilet.'

Another sigh. 'Albert, we've spoke about this before, haven't we? It'll get seen to soon enough, Albert.'

'Beryl? Beryl! Get me my pills, Beryl love. Sorry, sir, did you say something?'

'For heaven's sake, Albert, what is it?' And so on.

People and politics cannot wait to see the back of pensioners. They will say anything just so they'll get off the telephone. Anything. When the time was right, Albert would surface again, now that a relationship of sorts had been established. Oh, yes, Albert would be back.

The next morning, Dan rang me to let me know he had tracked down what he had been asked to get. 'Make a noise,' he advised, 'get out there and let them know there's a clumsy, undercover journalist out there.' It was time for our friend 'Stephen' to make another appearance.

I knew two councillors, one of whom had given the names of those who talked with World In Action. The other I had not yet contacted. This particular councillor did not like either John Prescott or John Black.

I began our conversation with the line, 'Let's talk about our friend in Manchester [meaning the man from TV].' I was met with an enthusiastic response, to say the least. I had already checked him out with a stalwart Labour man, and he said that the council-lor was as straight as a die. Within a few minutes, we had arranged to meet the next day, and he signed off with a cryptic line of his own. 'I knew you were here,' he said, pleased with the fact.

I got to his house, an anonymous-looking place, and he opened the door. He was shocked. I am half-Arab, my father originally coming from Saudi Arabia but it was not this that surprised him. It was the fact that we had met before, some time ago, when he knew me as a freelance journalist.

He regained his composure pretty quickly and invited me in. I could see him desperately trying to say something to put himself at ease. He had, in the past, struck me as a little paranoid, and my appearance seemed to exacerbate this tendency. I knew what he was thinking – fucking hell, I'd better not piss this guy off. He'll probably ride past on his camel and bomb my house – and I let him think that. I imagined the last thing he heard from me was the letter from the Deputy Iranian Ambassador. But that's for another time.

He led me into the living room and we talked, with me know-ing that every tiny little detail would be spread like wild fire among the local councillors.

All I can really say about that conversation is that I had never in my life been so unbelievably, staggeringly, bored out of my skull. Committees, loss of grants, motions – all stupendously dull, and I wanted to get out of there so badly. I was just about to make my excuses when, out of nowhere, he went from droning on and on about committee meetings to a stream of most unreal, slan-derous bullshit about what some local councillors got up to when the day's business was over. This one was fucking that one's wife, that one was in a bisexual affair; and so on. I was after informa-tion, but not this kind. I do not know why he was talking like that, but it was such obvious bullshit I had to leave. According to this guy, Hull City council made Caligula's court look like a village fête.

I practically ran to my car when he finally wrapped things up.

'Hope to hear from you soon, my friend,' he said, as friendly as can be. I smiled and got into my car, thinking he must be joking.

As I drove home, I told myself that the meeting had not been a total loss: he was what was known as a 'revolving door', leading to nowhere in particular, although in time he might prove to be useful. He was still close to John Prescott on the political grapevine, and his bitterness towards him (and, I had gathered, others on the Council) meant that we could feed him information, and see what would get through.

Chapter Ten

B y now, we had managed to create links with several sources of information, both in and out of Hull. There was World In Action, of course, the two Hull councillors, one of whom was convinced that local politics was a smoke screen for debauchery, and, thanks to Albert, there was the source very close to John Prescott himself.

We were all due to meet on Friday, and I was hoping they'd all have done what they had been told to do. In the meantime, I was determined to cement the links with World In Action. We had already arranged to meet, but I did not want this to go off the boil so, reversing the charges once more, I gave him a call.

I used it as an excuse to finalise the details of where we would be meeting. I had asked him if he would come to Hull, but he told me that this was 'out of the question, at the moment,' so we agreed to meet at the Granada Television Studio's in Manchester. He told me that he would pick up the expenses for the trip, so naturally the offer seemed fair enough. While we were sorting all that out, he asked me a question. 'Have you heard anything about any other journalist being in Hull?'

I answered: 'No, why?'

'Well,' he said, 'I don't know if you read The Independent, but there was an article in there recently, written by a journalist called Christian Woolmer. I just wondered if you'd read it that's all. 'I had to admit, I had not. Long words tend to give me headache.

'Get hold of a copy,' the World In Action man said, 'It's very interesting.'

We spoke about the 'political scene' in Hull for a few minutes, and he asked me if I knew Councillor John Black. I told him no, I did not, although I knew of him, and his political reputation. 'To be honest,' I said, 'I know little about what goes on in the Council (unless you count the alleged sexual athletics of some of them, I thought, recalling the previous day's fiasco), and I rarely read the local rag.

'All I know of, with any real certainty, is that there's a lot of jealousy and in-fighting at the Council. That, and a police investigation.

'You've got to understand something,' I told him, 'John Black is a very good friend of John Prescott. A lot of political backbiting goes on, and many are jealous of Black having such a powerful ally. Effectively, he has access to the Government.'

'Yes,' came the reply, 'and he certainly seems to have plenty to do. He's on the Housing Committee Trust Board.'

I listened to him and noted that he knew exactly what he was talking about. This guy, I remember thinking, had definitely done his research. How long had he really been in Hull to find all this out?

'That's true,' I said, 'but that's John Black for you. From what I've heard, he's a real go-getter.'

The World In Action reporter laughed. 'You almost sound as if you're defending him,' he said.

'No, I'm just telling you as it is. Black is Prescott's friend, and that means ego trouble from other politicians in his party; and that can mean rumours, envy, you name it.'

There was a pause, then World In Action said: 'I just don't understand, though, why Prescott would defend Black so staunchly. Surely, he'd be better off just keeping his head down while the shit flew in Black's direction?'

'Maybe it's just a case of good old-fashioned loyalty,' I answered, 'friendships can exist in politics, you know.'

World In Action sighed. 'Perhaps.'

The phone call over, I decided to ring Jim. I hadn't asked Jim to do anything the previous day, and although he had been a wanker on the night out, it was only the drink talking. Normally, he was a pretty okay sort of bloke, so I reneged on my earlier thoughts of cutting him out of the project.

His first words were, 'Oh no, don't tell me Friday's piss-up is off!'

'Don't fret, Fireman Sam, you'll get to hose down some more shrubbery.'

'Oh yeah, sorry about that. Nature calls and all that.' He sounded sheepish.

'But did you have to answer to it near a certain Deputy Prime Minister's house?' I asked, wondering why I had even bothered ringing in the first place.

'No, and again, I'm sorry.' He at least sounded genuine.

'Well,' I said, accepting his apology, 'here's how you can redeem yourself...' I asked Jim to put out some feelers about the club that World In Action had mentioned, and I told him to get as much information as possible by Friday's meeting.

Jim's answer was no surprise. 'By Friday?' He practically screamed down the phone at me.

'That's when we're meeting,' I said, coolly. 'All right, I'm on it,' he said, and he put the phone down.

Over the next few days I busied myself with calling up a few councillors and having a nice little chin-wag. We all had decided, in our own ways, to put on our hob-nail boots and start storming around a very delicate political situation. It was an old psychological trick we had used in the group, whereby we simply let the person or organisation in question know that there was somebody there.

This was where the mysterious 'Stephen' would really come into it. With five blokes stomping around, all asking questions, finding information, all giving the name 'Stephen', it would look for all the world like some sort of ubiquitous, super-journalist was in the area, and being one very busy boy. If there was a house of cards in Hull, nothing would unnerve its architects than the thought that someone was intent on blowing on it.

Another reason for doing things this way was to get the right people communicating. When people talk, they move information that might otherwise stay locked within the inner circles of the local politicians. We anticipated it would not be very long before our enigmatic friend's presence became known to the person we were targeting.

Friday came, and I was feeling both pleased and anxious. Pleased because I really felt we were getting somewhere, and anxious because we might all meet up and the hot topic of conversation might be that the pub was all out of salt and vinegar crisps.

I knew Dan had something and, before we were due to meet, I was to get copies of the planning file my friend had kindly made for me; but as far as I knew the rest of the group might have spent the last few days playing pocket billiards.

I arrived at the pub, fresh from collecting the planning file copies, five minutes after eight and was surprised to find everyone already there, drinking, talking, and having a high old time.

'Pint is it?' said Dan as I approached the table. 'It certainly is,' I replied, smacking my lips.

'Well, then, there's the bar,' he grinned and held up his empty glass, 'and mine's a pint as well.'

'Clever bastard!' I thought to myself, getting the drinks in, and I only hoped that he had been half that smart when it came to him doing what I had asked of him. Drinks in hand, I joined everybody. I sat down next to Malcolm, who was not looking happy. The rest – Dan, Harry and Jim – were all at the other side of the table, and we both sat facing them. I took a swig of my pint.

'What's up with you?' I asked Malcolm, and everyone else started sniggering. Harry piped up. 'It's his old lady,' he said, and I remembered Malcolm telling me he had 'women trouble'.

'We're all commiserating with him; he's been exiled from the conjugal bed,' said Dan.

'I thought you and your missus had a double,' said Jim, to which Malcolm replied: 'Leave it, will you? I only told you – he pointed an accusatorial finger at Harry – and you've told every fucker!'

He shook his head and went to the bar, empty glass in hand. I followed. 'What's up with you and your old lady, then,' I asked as he ordered a drink. Malcolm looked at me and shook his head again. 'Oh, nothing. I don't really want to go into it,' he said, and I thought, fair enough.

Malcolm turned to me and said, 'See her?' – he nodded in the direction of the barmaid.

'Yeah, so?'

'She's been giving me the eye all night, she has.'

'You've only been here half an hour,' I replied, as she handed Malcolm his drink and change. He smiled at me. 'She definitely fancies me, I can tell.'

We both went back to the table. It was not the first time a barmaid found Malcolm irresistible. In fact, he could not enter a pub without a female falling for him, staff or customer. The more I thought about it, the more I was sure it was directly connected to his lack of action on the home front, and I wondered how long this 'woman trouble' of his had really been going on for. I put it down to the 'full sack syndrome' and left it at that.

As we sat, Dan tapped his glass with his keys. 'Order, order, gentlemen! Can we call this meeting to order!' he yelled.

'Ian, can I be Health Secretary?' grinned Jim. Harry butted in.

'No way, I'm Health Secretary; you can be...' he thought for a minute 'what can Jim be, Ian?'

'You can be out on your arse, both of you, if you keep carrying on like daft sods,' I snapped.

The words rolled off Jim's back like so much water. 'Ah, you're only jealous because I'm Health Secretary!'

'No, I am!' shouted Harry.

I lent over the table, and brought my voice down low. 'Enough of this clowning around, all right?' I looked at Harry and Jim when I said this. 'Any more of this shit,' I continued, 'and I'll reshuffle the pair of you out. Got that?'

Malcolm spoke, breaking the silence. 'Here we are,' he said, and he stood up and pulled up something out of a carrier bag that he had under the table. He slapped them down in the middle of the table.

'Fuckin' hell,' Harry exclaimed.

'Impressed?' asked Malcolm.

'No,' Harry replied, 'you nearly knocked my pork scratchings over.'

It had been Malcolm's job to get John Prescott's and John Black's Land Registry documents, and it certainly seemed as if he had completed that task successfully.

The papers on the table, Malcolm spoke. 'I'll tell you something interesting,' Malcolm began.

'I knew if I waited long enough you finally would,' joked Harry.

Malcolm shot him a look, then continued. 'Both them documents show both Prescott and Black have bought land off the Council. Why are they both buying land off the council?' he asked.

I picked the two documents up and examined them. Both said 'Deeds of Grant,' along with 'Hull City Council'. I remember thinking they looked very ordinary.

Jim had a moment of lucidity. 'I knew Black had bought some land to build his house,' he said, 'but I never knew it was Council land.'

'What about Prescott?' I asked Malcolm, 'what did he want the land for?'

Dan interjected. 'I don't know about that,' he said, 'but I've given Prescott's house a good looking over,' and with that he pulled from his jacket pocket some papers with hand-written notes all over them. He carried on talking as he looked down at the scribble. 'Prescott's house,' he said, and he had our attention, 'used to belong to people who were in the Salvation Army. I've actually spoken to one of them, and they had an interesting time while they were there. The occupiers, believe it or not, were a religious group of some sort, who claimed that they had received a calling from God to set up a commune.'

We were all listening intently, even Harry, who was chewing his pork scratchings in respectful silence. Dan flipped over a piece of paper and started to recite. It was certainly a fascinating story, all about how they took inspiration from a group of religious charismatics in the United States. Eventually they had held some meetings in Hull to raise money through what they called 'faith loans' so they could buy the house.

Needless to say, the Salvation Army did not take too kindly to this, and so they parted company with the group who managed to raise the money. A commune was born where they grew their own food, and even ran a small building supplies company. To cut a long story short, their Eden was short-lived and the house was put back on the market, with the group trying to repay the 'faith loans' they had raised. The house was put up for sale with a local estate agent, and the Prescotts, it seemed, were eager to buy it.

'The person I spoke to,' said Dan, 'reckoned the Prescott's paid

£28,000.' He continued. 'I also tracked down the people who bought Prescott's old house situated on Sutton Park. They did buy it off him for £28,000, apparently.'

We were all still silent. Dan looked at his papers, at us and then shrugged. 'That's it,' he said, simply.

'The end.' Harry said, 'That was great, Dan. Now tell us the one about the three bears.'

I passed the documents around the table, and Jim was looking at them when he said: 'It says here that Prescott's got a mortgage with Lloyd's Bank. I suppose he banks with them as well.'

'So what?' Dan said, 'If you're thinking what I'm thinking, don't bother. He's the Deputy Prime Minister, for fuck's sake, there'll be 'anti-browse' on his file.'

Dan had been active, there was no denying that, and he knew what he was talking about. Jim smiled. 'Just a thought,' he said.

I turned to Malcolm, who was eyeing up the barmaid. 'Oi, Casanova,' I said, bringing out of his hormone-induced haze, 'did you get hold of the actual Deeds of Grant?' Malcolm shook his head. 'No, you can only get them through a solicitor, and he has to provide a good reason for wanting them.'

'We have; bringing down the Government,' grinned Jim. Nobody rose to that.

'So we can't get them at all?' I asked. Dan interjected again. 'We'll get them, won't we, Malcolm?' and a sly grin spread across his face.

'Now, now,' I said, 'don't you two even think of getting hold of documents in an illegal fashion. I simply won't be having any kind of naughtiness here.'

'Neither would we,' Dan said, 'and I'm upset that you would even say something like that to me.'

'That's all right, then,' I said, pointing to the pair of them, 'as long as we all understand each other.' They both nodded, as did everyone else. Harry slapped his hands together. 'Who's round is it?' he asked. 'Never mind that,' I said, 'Anyone else got anything?'

I stared straight at Jim and Harry. No answer. Jim was first to speak. He cleared his throat. 'Ah, well, not much luck, to be honest. I mean,' he cleared his throat again, 'it's not like we had much time, is it?' He looked at Dan when he said this, which did not exactly back up his point. Dan had performed miracles in the few days we had.

Jim fell silent, deciding on less talk and more drink, as he lifted his glass and took a sip. Then Harry asked me how I had fared. I told them, and, bless them, they heard me out before pissing themselves with laughter. They especially liked the part about Hull City Council being a branch of the Hellfire Club – allegedly.

Harry got up to get the drinks in, and as he was standing at the bar waiting to be served, I noticed him making a 'come over' motion with his hand. I went over. 'Listen,' he whispered, 'I have got something to show, but not here.'

I was puzzled. 'But this is where we meet, you silly sod!' Harry grimaced. 'Look, the thing is…' I could feel it coming. 'I don't want to meet. Not with him around, anyway.'

The drinks came and, as Harry busied himself with paying, I looked back at the others. 'Who are you on about?' I asked Harry, taking hold of some of the drinks.

Harry nodded towards the table. 'Fuckin' Arthur Scargill over there,' he said. 'I'm afraid you'll have to be a tad more specific,' I said.

Harry rolled his eyes. 'Malcolm!' he gasped, exasperated, 'I don't trust his big gob.' This surprised me. Malcolm was a prat at times, but he was a good-hearted, as well, and he would never blow it for us. At least, not intentionally.

'Are you saying you want out?'

'What? No! Not at all. It's just can't we meet without him? Some of the time at least?'

I was lost in thought for a second. I did not fancy bullshitting Malcolm.

'You and me, for instance,' continued Harry, 'we can meet. Tomorrow, at my house? It's just that maybe I'm getting nervous. I don't know him well enough.'

What could I say? I nodded my head in agreement.

'I've got nothing against the lad, I just don't know him that well,' he added.

'All right,' I said, 'I'll be there,' and we marched back to the tables as if nothing had happened. It was now my turn to 'show and tell,' and out came the letters from the planning file. They showed that the club had obtained grants through the Department of the Environment for the purpose of training unemployed people for the catering and service industry.

'Hey,' Malcolm said to Dan, 'maybe you can get a job with them!'

Dan, bizarrely, did not burst out laughing at this, and Harry shot me a 'see what I mean?' look. The night degenerated but I was happy; we had begun accomplishing things, we had a direction to go in, we understood what we had to do.

At the end of the evening, Harry collected everything, and we went our separate ways once more. I did not want to speak with Harry behind Malcolm's back, but if that was necessary, then so be it. I would have to chalk it up as another little sacrifice.

Chapter Eleven

In the end, I went to Harry's the following Wednesday, and in the meantime, things were quiet on both the work and home fronts. Thanks to my girlfriend, 'Chez Newton' was officially a 'no political scams, you bastard' zone. As for work, Gus and Joe were the same as ever, although my relationship with them had changed somewhat. Things were a little frosty, which I regretted. I suppose it was to be expected, having asked the two of them to do something that was, to them, plainly crazy. Where once we would have talked about this and that, joked with each other, gone for a coffee during break, there was now a forced 'all right?' and that was more or less it.

Gus was particularly hard work, and was potentially a pain as he thought it was all over. If one of us were to spill anything by accident, he would be justifiably angry that he had been lied to. You can't yank a guy like Gus's chain and expect not to get your arm torn off. He would, I was certain, grass us all up, maybe not out of spite but from sheer pig-headedness and hurt pride. With Joe, it was simpler – I think he looked at the situation, and worked out a straight forward equation: fucking around equals losing your job and that was that.

One Wednesday, when we had just come off four days of nights, I pulled up outside Harry's place. I felt half dead, and when he opened the door I could see that he was looking just as fresh and radiant as myself.

The house was a pigsty, typical of a man who works nights. The kitchen door was wide open, and I could see pots and plates, all filthy, rising to the ceiling. The living room had no carpet, and the floor boards were visible either side of a dirty rug.

Empty lager cans were strewn all over the coffee table and, as we sat down on the sofa, I hoped that I would not get wet.

'Well,' I said, 'I always wondered why your lass didn't live with you, and the last piece of the puzzle just clicked into place.' Harry turned and looked around the room.

'What, do you think the place is a mess?' He looked hurt.

'Oh no, I think empty fag packets are an excellent alternative to carpets.' Harry slunk into the sofa, then sat up again quickly, excited.

'Oh yeah, the stuff!' He got up and went into the kitchen. He returned a second later with some scrunched up bits of paper in his hand. I had told him not to mention anything at work and so he had, in case he forgot, made notes.

He unfolded the papers and glanced through them.

'I spoke to those councillors you told me to,' he said, not taking his eyes off the papers.

'Oh yeah? Go on.'

'Well, I didn't get much out of them, as you can imagine. But I did get something quite interesting.'

'What?'

'There's another journalist in Hull, helping World In Action.' I was very surprised by this.

'Go on,' I said, curious for more.

Harry continued. 'He's a local guy, his name is…' Harry flipped over one, then two pieces of paper, as if trying to find something. 'I can't find his name. It's something like Doyle, or Boyle. Yeah, that's it – Dylan Boyle.'

I had never heard of him and I told Harry this. Harry thought for a moment, then: 'Oh, of course! You know! He's a right fuckin' tosser! Reads the cricket scores on local radio!' Harry shook his head. 'Yeah, I remember now. He listens to councillor's whinge and gripe, and then he passes it off as red-hot information. He's freelance, shows visiting journalists around Hull.'

I was still none the wiser. A short while later, I would mention his name to a journalist on a leading broadsheet newspaper, and get the reply that Mr Boyle was, to put it politely, 'not very impressive.' 'Is that it?' I asked, 'that covers two pages of notes?'

'No,' Harry answered, 'one's the shopping list.' I decided to leave, so I made up some story and I cleared off home. Harry could be real hard work.

'Hey, what are you and your old lady doing Friday night?' said Dan over the phone. I told him: 'The usual – pub, take away, fill our faces, bed. That, or a night of Flamenco. It depends on how we're feeling. Why?'

'There's a big bunch of us going out on the piss; me, the ball and chain, and some mates I used to work with. They're coming over from Leeds. Come with us,' he said, 'it'll be a laugh.'

'Okay,' I said, wondering if it would be a laugh, 'what time?'

'Meet us here, say eight?' I mulled it over in my mind. Dan was not the most sober of people, and his friends, I feared, might be the same. But at the same time, I fancied a change from the same old routine. 'See you Friday,' I said, hoping I would not regret it.

Friday night came, and my good lady and I were on time. Dan and his girlfriend, were waiting for us at the top of his street. We strolled up to them.

'We're all meeting in town,' said Dan, 'so let's get going!' We got to the pub where we were all due to meet, and I was shocked. There were about twelve people in total, all waving and shouting over to us, already pissed out of their heads!

No wonder Dan was so eager to get there; they were all like him, booze-obsessed. I saw my girlfriend look at me with a classic 'what the fuck have you got us into?' stare, but I shrugged it off. The night was young, and I was sure that they would calm down as the evening wore on. At least, that was what I kept telling myself.

Dan introduced me to everyone, and I quickly forgot their names. I've got to hand it to them, they weren't tight when it came to getting the drinks in, and in no time at all I was as near as damn it paralytic.

I can recall bits of the evening – seeing my girlfriend and Dan's talking at the bar; a fat bloke in a loud shirt dancing and smacking someone flying; a young girl in the group spilling a drink on herself, and laughing. But nothing in particular happened – until we went to a night-club

We all trooped to the club, the cold wind sobering us up – kind of – and we lined up outside in the queue. Dan stood next to me, and folded his arms against the chill.

'Well?' he said, expectantly.

'Well what?' I asked, desperate to get inside for some warmth.

'They're all right, aren't they?'

'Yeah. I didn't think there'd be so many, though. What did you used to do? Play in a rugby team?'

'Nah, none of them are fuckin' hard enough for that. None of the blokes anyway.' The line started to move as the club began letting people in. I've never known why night-clubs make you wait outside; someone must think that nothing gets people in the party mood more than freezing their nuts off beforehand.

Two minutes or so later and we were all at the bar. I had spoken to some of Dan's friends, but it was hard work talking to someone when they were drunk. Besides, I had the Council thing so much in my head that I was scared I might accidentally used that classic line, 'have you been talking to World In Action?' – always a great icebreaker.

We broke off into little splinter groups. I sat at a small table in one of the corners with Dan; a big sod called Steve, and his girl-friend. Everyone else was either dancing, at the bar or I presume, having themselves a big piss.

We talked, our heads thumping in time to the music as it screamed out of the walls. The lights in there would kill an epileptic in three seconds flat. Dan practically had to yell at the top of his voice in order to be heard.

'This is Ian!' he shouted to Steve (at least, I think his name was Steve), and his girlfriend. They both nodded in synch' with each other.

Dan turned to me, yelling: 'Get them in, and I'll see you later!'

He was up and off, straight onto the dance floor. I had never seen Dan acting like it; he was gone, his arms and legs all separate entities. He looked over to me at the bar and waved. He was in his element, and as I went back to the table with the drinks, I turned back and saw that he had been joined Steve's girlfriend, who was just as rhythmically deprived.

Steve picked up Dan's drink and there was no way I was going to stop him. He took a real long swig, nodded and sat in silence.

Then we started to talk. We gassed about this and that, he told me about his car and I told him about World In Action.

Oops.

It was a stupid thing to do, but my brain was being run on alcohol now, and what it sent to my mouth had nothing to do with me. I told him the lot. Everything. But then he said something that, even in my drunken state, I could not believe.

He pointed a wobbly finger at the dance floor. 'See my lass?' he slurred.

'Uh? Yeah. What's up?' I replied.

'She was on the phone to John Prescott only the other day.'

He did not look like an A-bomb, but that was what he was; his words wiped clear all booze from my bloodstream and straightened me up in my chair; I was staggered.

'What?! Why? Who does she work for?' I wanted to know everything.

He moved his head slowly, and said: 'The Gas Board in Leeds.'

Perfectly timed, the two others walked back to the table. Dan
was soaked with sweat and as he sat down I could read the expression on his face.

'Where's my fuckin' drink?' he spat, glaring at me.

'Come on,' I said, standing, 'I'll get you one in, it's my round.'
Dan heaved himself up and we went to the bar. The queue was
unreal, but I was glad; it gave us time to talk. I told him what Steve
had just told me, and his face ran the gamut: surprise, disbelief,
puzzlement, and, finally, elation that something like this had fallen
into our laps.

He laughed. 'I cannot fuckin' believe what you've just told me!'
he said.

'You and me both,' I replied, 'this is too good an opportunity
to fuck up, so hurry up and get the drinks in, Steve'll have what
you're having, and his lass likes lager and lime. I'll have my usual.
Cheers.'

'I thought it was your round,' protested Dan.

'Don't be so petty, Dan, I've got to get back to the table and
find out all I can.'

I left Dan in the queue for the bar, and sat back down at the
table. Steve looked like he was about to collapse, and his girlfriend did not look best pleased to be sat there without a drink.
By now, I couldn't see anyone else from the group, not even my
old lady. Maybe someone stole her away from me. A stupid idea; I
wouldn't have two strokes of good luck in one evening.

I attempted small talk with Steve's girlfriend. I wanted to pump
her for information; preferably before she poured another lager
and lime down her neck; if she got any more pissed than she

already was we were sunk.

I had to tread carefully. I did not want Steve thinking I was trying to pull his bird so I started small, or at least that was the plan. 'So, do you like Hull?' I said to her, and a second later Dan arrived with two drinks in his hands. He said to her: 'What's this about you talking to John Prescott, then, eh?' This seemed to grab her attention, and she became more animated, whilst her beau slumped, head forward, onto the table.

'I'll be right back,' Dan said and raced off to fetch the other two drinks.

I smiled wanly at Steve's girlfriend, thinking: 'have we blown it?' Dan returned, and took his seat next to me.

'What was you on about?' she said nursing her drink.

'I was just saying,' Dan continued, 'You work at the Gas Board, yeah?' She nodded. 'Yeah, so what?' I wanted to jump in, ask her in a more round about way, more subtly; but Dan was in full flow and there was no stopping him. Well, if we were all sober there would have been, but we were three sheets to the wind and my mouth had stopped working properly. I guessed Dan knew what to do, and so sat back and listened.

'Your Steve said you were talking to John Prescott, is that right?' asks Dan.

She giggles. 'Oh aye, yeah! I said to him, "Are you the Deputy Prime Minister?" and he says "No, that's my father," and I thought, what a fucking small world!' Trying to be nonchalant about it, Dan asked: 'What did he want?' Steve's girlfriend looked pained, thinking back. Then she giggled again.

'Oh, he's always on the phone, about something or other.' She thought again, then: 'He wanted some gas work doing in a house, and I thought, fuckin' hell, it'd better be done quick!'

Dan smiled at her. 'What, his house?'

'No!' she blurted, 'look, I've spoken to him a few times, that's all.' I did not know whether she was getting pissed off with all the questions by then, or whether she did not really know that much, but I had the distinct feeling we should leave it alone. Then laughing boy came to all of a sudden, making my mind up for me.

Steve said: 'Hey, are you going to sell all this to World In Action, then, or what?' His girlfriend looked at him as if he had gone off the deep end.

'What are you fuckin' on about, Steve? We're just having a laugh. You remember me telling you about when John Prescott's son rang up, don't you?'

His face was blank, and sweat soaked. 'Of course I do, I told these two, you silly sod!' Steve's girlfriend glared at the two of us, and I stared back at her, and at the brick shithouse sat next to her. I thought maybe that look my old lady gave me was not so stupid after all.

'What's our share of this, eh?' said Steve.

'What? World In Action aren't paying us, you idiot!' Dan replied.

To this, Steve leant to his girlfriend and said, 'Don't you tell 'em fuck all! Greedy bastards!' I stepped in at this point, eager to clear matters up before we got our chairs rammed up our arses.

'If we make anything, we'll give you five percent,' I said, and I could feel Dan's eyes burning into me as I said it.

Steve shook his head. 'No fuckin' way! Ten! Ten percent or you can both fuck off out of it!' Dan suddenly must have been feeling strong; maybe it was the drink, or maybe he had been spinning on his head too much on the dance floor.

'Five, or you can go back to Leeds, you grasping fucker!' This did not have the result I expected, i.e. we were both still alive, and Steve seemed to calm down. 'Okay, five it is.' He pointed to Dan, 'don't disappoint me,' and he got up and went over to the toilets. We sat there in silence for a moment when a couple of people we had been sitting with in the pub came over and started to talk to Steve's girlfriend.

They whisked her onto the dance floor, leaving Dan and I to talk.

'What a disaster!' I said.

'Not to worry, I'll bypass Steve.' He looked over to the dance floor.

'I'm off for a boogie, you stay with the big fella, I'm going to get the goods.' Dan strode off. I was feeling a little dejected. Steve's girlfriend could fill in some big gaps, but her boyfriend was in the way. I turned to the dance floor. Dan was getting on down, and bending Steve's girlfriend's ear at the same time. What a guy! I only hoped he could get us what we needed - if we knew what that was exactly.

I decided not to sit and wait for 'Lurch' to return from his ablutions, so I hauled my drunken ass over to another table. I watched Dan talk to Steve's girlfriend for around five minutes, and then he came over to where I was.

'Listen to this,' he said, sitting, 'I've got her to ring me in a couple of weeks. She told me the name of Prescott Junior's company – kind of.'

'What do you mean, kind of?'

Dan said, 'She can't remember exactly. Don't forget, she's pissed. She said the company is called Tyke, or Dyke, or maybe Mike, she doesn't know. Fuck, she doesn't know what day of the week it is at the moment.'

'Have you made a deal with her or something?' I asked, and Dan craned his head forward.

'What? You'll have to speak up a bit, I can't hear a thing.'

His hearing was fine a moment ago, but I left the matter there.

DUSTBINGATE!

Dan could take care of this little episode all on his own, he was a big boy. I decided I had had enough. Normally, I could not get enough of over-priced, watered-down drinks, music that drowns out your own thoughts, and queues for the toilets longer than those to get into Disneyworld, but not that night. The time was close to half past two and I was exhausted. I told Dan this and he laughed.

'You're getting past it, Ian.' he said, and I had to agree.

'Where is everyone?' I asked, looking around the club. It was heaving with people, none of whom I recognised.

'I dunno,' answered Dan, 'I saw my lass and yours having a right good chin-wag about half an hour ago, but that's it.' He took a swig of his drink and shrugged. 'I wouldn't worry about it.' Dan tapped me on the shoulder. 'There you are,' he said, as my old lady came walking over, along with Dan's girlfriend.

'Time we was off, eh?' I said to my partner, and she nodded.

I turned to Dan. 'We're off. I'll be in touch.' We left them there, with a good half an hour of partying to go before chucking out time. The journey home was in hindsight, frosty with my partner hardly speaking, except for the occasional 'yes', 'no' and 'uh-huh'. We stopped on the way for a pizza to take home and I was blissfully unaware of any domestic problems until we were safely inside the house. I went to a cupboard and took out two plates.

'How much pizza do you want?' I asked, placing them on the kitchen counter.

'Here!' came her voice and the next thing I knew, the pizza was out of it's box and flying towards me. They certainly make those things perfectly round sometimes, because it rocketed at me like a discus. The pizza crashed to the ground, splattering all over the floor, cheese and tomato everywhere, some of it landing on my shoes.

'You stupid bastard!' I shouted, 'what the fuck was that all about? Was it the wrong topping?'

'Don't you get clever with me, you shifty shit!' She moved in closer, her hands rolled into fists. 'Guess who I got talking to tonight? Go on, have a guess.'

'I don't know! Love.'

'Don't you fuckin' 'love' me. I was talking to Dan's girlfriend, and she told me something very interesting.'

'Oh? What?' I knew pretending to be innocent would only get her more irate, but I did not know what else to do.

'You're up to something, aren't you?' she barked, 'aren't you?'

I laughed. 'I don't know what the hell you're on about. Honestly.'

'Oh?' she said, 'So you're not talking to World In Action, then? You haven't been going around to councillor's houses? You haven't been doing any of that? Don't lie to me, Ian! Fuckin' Prescott! He'll have you for dinner!'

'I can explain it all, love, honest!' I said, but it was the last dying gasps of a man who knew it was all over, and I had to face the consequences.

She leaned in close, inches away from me. If she were a cartoon character, she would have had steam coming out of her ears.

'What did I tell you after last time. Eh? What did I say? I said, if you ever even tried another one of your little political scams, I'd throw you out.' She was close to boiling point and something big was heading my way. The pizza was just a warning shot. A frankly scary smile appeared on her face.

'Fuck off,' she said, simply. 'Get out.' I was stunned.

'Don't be like that, love,' I protested, but she was having none of it.

'Go on, fuck off. I'm not kidding, Ian, take your political scams and get out of the house.' She certainly was not kidding.

'Go on,' she said firmly, 'you and your political scams!' I looked sadly at her. Then at the pizza. I was starving.

I went upstairs and packed some things. The essentials – tooth-brush, a few clothes, tobacco – and, as I got to the bottom of the stairs, she was waiting, front door open.

'Car keys,' she said, holding out her hand.

'What? How am I supposed to get around?' I said, wishing I was tucked up in bed. 'The bike,' was all she said.

'I'm not riding about on a bike at three in the morning!' I yelled.

'Fine,' she replied, 'push the fucker. Just get it and get out. I'm having the car.'

The next thing I knew, I was on my bike – literally. I wasn't sure where I could go; I knew plenty of people, but turning up in the middle of the night wanting to sleep on their couch would not go down too well with most of them. There was only one place.

I remember biking past Prescott's house in the dead of night with a freezing wind blowing up my arse. I could not help a grunt of derision as I rode by. 'This is all your fault Prescott.'

'What the fuck are you doing here?' exclaimed Harry as he opened his front door.

'It's a long story, mate.' I said, 'Can I stay here a few days?' Harry sighed. 'You'd better, I suppose. I guess this means the cat's out of the bag, eh? I'm sorry to hear that, mate.' I pushed my bike up into the hallway.

Harry sniffed the air.

'Ian,' he said, 'have you been eating pizza?'

Chapter Twelve

The next morning, Harry handed me a cup of tea while I laid on his couch, with a single blanket over me. It was ten in the morning, and only seven hours ago I was in my house, happy as can be, about to eat. Then what happened? My supper turns into a Frisbee, my girlfriend throws me out, and I'm riding half way across the city on a knackered push-bike in search of board and lodgings. It was certainly a memorable night out.

I thought about my drunken chat with Steve. On the face of things, telling him everything should have been a very stupid thing to do, but it had turned out to be very fortuitous. Had it not been for my inebriated state, we would never have known about this lead. I had been lucky; we had been put on a path we would have known nothing about had it not been for my inebriated state. But I was not exactly in a mood to pat myself on the back. My domestic life was a tragedy. A perfectly good pizza going to waste like that. What was I going to do now?

'Morning,' Harry said, handing me the cup. 'You all right there on the couch?'

'Yeah,' I said, the events of a few hours ago replaying in my head, 'I'm fine.'

'You don't look fine. You look like shit,' said Harry.

I sat up and took a sip of tea while Harry opened the curtains. Grey skies as usual.

'Maybe you should get yourself round to your house, get it sorted – quick.'

'I tell you what, you go and get the frying pan and smack me. Save me the journey home for it. That's all I'll be getting.'

'She's not like that!'

'No, she isn't,' I agreed. 'It's all my fault, let's face it. Nah, I'd better leave it for a few days, let it simmer.'

Harry sat on the arm of a chair. 'You know what she's like, and

DUSTBINGATE!

I can't honestly say that I blame her. She doesn't need it – neither do you.' He stood up again. 'Don't tell me you've forgotten what happened last time? You were out the front door so fast you didn't know what had hit you.'

'I know what hit me this time,' I said, 'a twelve inch meat feast.'

Harry held up his hands. 'Don't go any further,' he said, 'what two consenting adults get up to in the privacy of their own home is their business.'

'You mucky-minded bastard, it's a pizza!'

'I certainly hope so,' was his reply as he walked into the kitchen.

The phone rings.

'Hello?' says the source.

'Oh, good morning to you, sir. It's Albert, sir – Albert Gunner.' There is a very large sigh.

'Albert, yes. What is it, Albert?'

'Well, sir. I'm ringing about my toilet. It's, pardon my language, sir, but it's flaming well buggered.'

'Albert,' the source answered wearily, 'don't call me 'sir,' I haven't been knighted. You've told me all this and I told you only a few days ago, didn't I? I said, it'll be fixed.'

'Yes, sir, you did at that, sir.'

The source says, 'Albert, you forgot to give me a phone number. Give me a number I can contact you on, eh?' Silence. 'Albert?' says the source, 'Are you still there? Albert?'

'Oh, sorry, sir, I think I nodded off for a minute there. Was I gone long?'

'Oh, for fuck's sake, Albert!' says the source.

I was due to meet World In Action soon, and I wondered if I

should. I was already sleeping on a couch that Harry had scored from one of the finest skips in Hull – how much lower could I go? Would I ever be allowed home? It was the foremost question in my mind. I would have to get back into the house, even if it was just to pick up my things and the material I needed for the meeting, but I was not looking forward to it.

I decided to head back to the house. Thankfully she hadn't confiscated my door keys, and there was no-one home. I slipped inside and collected what I needed for the meeting and left for Manchester.

A night on Harry's sofa was not exactly the best preparation for a major meeting, and I wasn't sure what I was going to say. I flicked idly through my magazine, while observing my fellow passengers. The train was full; screaming kids, commuters on mobiles, and, by the look of most of them, they were on Prozac pills as well.

When I got in, I made my way to Granada, and met my contact at reception. As I approached, I saw hesitation in World In Action's face, but I had been prepared for his reaction to my 'all year round tan'. It often happens that people don't expect my Arabian face after hearing my 'white' name. As we shook hands, I handed him something.

'What's this?' he said, taking it. It was my passport, or as I said to him, 'my British passport.' He passed it back to me, smiling.

He took me upstairs to the canteen, and I was surprised to find how small it was. Granada is where many of Britain's biggest television shows are produced, and I somehow expected something more spacious. I could see actors from famous shows coming and going, and it reminded me that fame is something concocted, unreal - they still had to queue for a ham sandwich and ask what the soup of the day was, just like us mere mortals.

We sat down, both of us with coffees, and it felt like being at the factory, well almost. He spoke first. 'I've been in Hull,' he said, and I could sense he was choosing his words carefully, 'and it's an interesting place, shall we say.' He took a sip of his coffee. He looked perturbed.

'The thing is, you – pow! – you, Ian suddenly appear out of nowhere, and you have to admit, that from my point of view, it's a bit disconcerting.'

'You've seen my passport,' I said. 'So let's not be having any Middle East conspiracies flying around, eh?'

World In Action nodded, understanding, but I could see he was still suspicious.

'For all I know,' he continued, 'you could be Secret Service.'

'No. I'm not,'

'I only ask because we deal with some very sensitive information here, and you might be after such information from me. You have to understand.'

I did. I was certainly not Secret Service, but I admitted that Allen, Terry, and I had a minor brush with the security services when we'd been caught in the middle of a political scam by Bradford police some years earlier. Again, that's another story.

World In Action listened, then asked: 'What's your angle?' It was a fair question, and I told him straight.

'I've always wanted to get into research, and this is a way in.' I also mentioned the other reason, money (although I didn't mention there was a group of us).

World In Action exhaled loudly. 'You're talking about splitting the Government! Hypothetically, you're talking about bringing it down! Why do you want to do that?'

'I don't!' I answered. 'If it leads to that, people will be scrambling to make names for themselves won't they?

'Maybe I'll be one of them.'

Now I was talking his language, and the real conversation finally began. He wanted to know how I had found out he was in Hull in the first place, and so I told him: his name, no doubt given in absolute secrecy, had been bounced about Hull like a rubber ball. I also told him that whatever he thought he had prised out of the councillors he had spoken to, most, if not all of it, had been vengeful bullshit.

'The last people who would know anything are the local councillors,' I said. 'Private business is never discussed with the local politicians!' I asked him if he knew Dylan Boyle, and he admitted he did. 'Yeah, he helped out.'

He asked, again, how I knew. I laughed. 'I just pricked up my ears. Hull's not the most politically subtle of places.'

All in all, we talked for around two hours, with people, famous and not so famous, coming and going while we spoke. The conversation complete, I handed over the documents we had gathered. He seemed quite taken aback, and told me he would make copies and return them as soon as he could. I said there would be more on the way.

As I got up to leave, he said to me, 'I'll try to get you on budget.' That was good enough for me. I thanked him, and we parted.

I got back to Harry's two and a half hours later. To my surprise, Dan was there, can in hand, and as I walked into the living room, he and Harry almost started jumping up and down.

'What happened?' Dan said, excitement in his voice.

'Whoa! Down, fella! Hang on, kids, Daddy's tired.' I then saw something out of the corner of my eye. 'Hey, get those empty fuckin' cans off my bed!' The couch had six or seven crushed cans on it. Dan rushed over and threw them on the coffee table. 'Well?' asked Harry.

Before I could answer, however, there was a knock at the door. Harry went to answer it. 'It's Jim, and he's brought cans.'

'Ian,' he beams, 'how did it go?' He perched himself next to Dan on the couch, and I told them how the meeting went. Everybody seemed happy with how things worked out, including myself. 'I've given him the documents,' I said, and then Dan cut in.

'Speaking of documents,' he said, and slapped the deeds of grant down onto the coffee table.

'They're the deeds of agreement between Prescott and the council, and between Black and the council; terms of the sale; who the land was sold to; all the amounts.' I picked them up. 'I'm going to get these fuckers in the post quick smart,' I said, 'I know someone who wants to see these.'

But Dan was not finished. Still smiling away to himself, he said, 'That's not all. Guess who I've been on the blower to?' I didn't need to guess.

'Fuckin' hell!' I said, surprised, 'There's no flies on you!'

Dan said, 'Nope. I've had a bath today.' He continued, the smile still there: 'My drinking buddy,' he corrected himself, 'no, my drinking buddy's lass – I couldn't be bothered to hang around, so I rang her. She got the goods.'

'And?'

'The name of the company Prescott Junior was ringing in regard to was Wyke Properties.'

'Never heard of them,' Harry said.

'Join the club,' Jim said.

'And that's not all,' said Dan, 'She's found something else, too. A "David Prescott" is building bungalows on Boardsman's Walk, Brandesburton.' This would later be shown to be nothing at all to do with the Prescotts we were looking at, but at the time, what turned out to be a coincidence got us excited.

'Get the telephone directory out, ' I said, 'look up Wyke Properties.'

Dan waved away the command with his hand. 'Already looked,' he said. 'There's fuck all listed. I've spent half the day ringing estate agents and property companies, as well, and that turned up zero too.'

'Are you sure?' I asked.

'Yeah,' He brightens up, 'but don't worry: she's working on an address.'

'You must be heading for a big bill,' said Jim, who had taken time out from guzzling beer.

Dan shook his head, and puts his hand into his jacket. 'Nah, not with this,' Dan said, and he pulled out a mobile phone.

'When did you get that?' asked Harry, who reached for it.

'Never mind that,' said Dan, 'I'm not using my house phone, no way.'

I did not see what he was getting at. 'Why not?' I asked, and Dan replied, 'Some of the councillors I've been talking to reckon the phones are tapped.' Everyone stared at him, then the phone, then back at him.

'You're fuckin' tapped,' I laughed, 'don't be so paranoid!'

Dan took the mobile back from Harry, and pocketed it. 'I'm not taking any risks,' he said, 'the fucker is tapped.'

Jim sat up. 'Any thoughts?' Harry asked him.

'What?' Jim replied. 'Oh. No, sorry, I just... I think I'm sat on a nail.'

Harry exclaimed, 'cheeky bastard!' and went into a sulk, staring at the floor.

'Hey,' said Dan, 'where's Malcolm?'

'Fuck knows,' muttered Harry. 'I'm telling you, if Malcolm gets pulled over this, he's going to sing like a canary.' He turned to me, and said, 'He will, I'm telling you.'

Jim broke in again. 'He won't!'

Harry glared at him. 'You what? Are you defending him? You and him are always at each other!'

Jim said, 'That's politics for you. We disagree on everything – so what? That's got fuck all to do with him as a person, has it? He's a good guy, Malcolm is. I like him.' Jim went back to sipping his can.

Harry looked shocked, embarrassed even. 'I like Malcolm, it's just, you know,' he seemed to be searching for the right words, 'I don't want to be a part of this with him, not with the mouth on him.'

Dan let out a chuckle. 'He certainly was in a funny mood the other night wasn't he?' he said, referring to Malcolm's lewdness.

'You'd better move that bike out of the hallway,' he continued, 'or else Malcolm won't be able to push the wheelbarrow he's lugging his balls around in past the front door.' Harry shrugged it all off. 'Look, I'll just say it once more. I do not want him knowing I'm involved – OK? I barely trust him with my phone number!' We all nodded.

In the end, it was decided, the 'real' meetings would feature Dan, Jim and Harry and myself. Some of us would still meet up with Malcolm as and when necessary; but as far as Malcolm was concerned, Harry had gone the way of Gus and Joe.

In fact, Harry would not be working with myself and Malcolm at the factory any more; he worked for an employment agency and he had been told he was being moved to another site. It was not, I concluded, anything personal between Harry and Malcolm: it was more a question of confidence.

Dan said, opening up another tin, 'I hope I don't get caught.

Look at what I've got to lose; holiday pay, sick pay, company pension – fuck, even the company car!'

'You're unemployed,' Jim said.

Dan swigged from his can. 'Oh yeah,' he sighed, 'I almost forgot.' We sat drinking, Jim's supplies being rapidly depleted.

'Oh, I meant to ask,' I said to Dan, 'Have we had any boomerangs back yet?' Dan spluttered, 'Oh, fuck, yeah!' He put down his can.

A 'boomerang' is a ploy whereby a titbit of information is given over the phone with subtle intimations attached; intimations, which make the listener's mind jump to many different (and usually wrong) conclusions. When the call is returned, hopefully the snippet will have more information attached to it.

'Listen to this,' Dan said. 'I've been talking to the locals. They reckon there's an Arab journalist on the prowl! Paranoid sods!' Dan continued. 'I'm telling you, Ian,' he said, 'by the time this is all over, you'll be the man on the grassy knoll.'

Harry looked concerned. 'Can't you...'

'Can't I what?' I said.

'Can't you get, you know, some political back-up?'

I knew what he was getting at. I raised an eyebrow. 'You mean talk to the "Ragheads" in London? I'll try.' I shook my head. I realised that Dan was not the only one who was tapped.

I thought about what Dan had just said. Local councillors and their paranoia; it was almost funny. But, I checked myself, later on this would all be very useful indeed.

DUSTBINGATE!

Chapter Thirteen

Our relationship with World In Action now established, we met twice more over as many weeks. Information was passed over, but to be frank it was small fry. Anything bigger had continued to elude us – until one morning when Dan received something through the mail.

I had stayed at Harry's as long as I could bear it, and was now at Dan's. His sofa was considerably softer – no slab of granite like Harry's, and as the poor bastard had nothing to do all day he kept a tidy place.

Communications with my partner had all but ground to a halt, and I did not want to look like I was rushing things. Pissing her off was a real stupid idea, especially when she was such a good shot with pizza. I decided to lie low while we were in the middle of the investigation, and Dan did not seem to mind.

I was asleep on his couch when the postman delivered the envelope one morning, and Dan bounced down the stairs. He tore it open, had a look inside, and woke me, saying with excitement in his voice, 'She's sent it! Look!' I opened my eyes slowly, not knowing what the hell he was on about.

'What? Who's sent what?' I asked, sitting up.

'Steve's bird, from the Gas Board in Leeds!' Dan looked it over and, even more excitedly said, 'It's got Prescott's name on it!' He went back to reading from it. 'It's about a house. Here, have a look.' I took the document and scanned through it, still half asleep. I saw the name 'John Prescott' and a local address next to it. I handed it back.

'Fuckin' hell, Ian,' Dan exclaimed, 'aren't you excited?'

'Yeah, I suppose so,' I answered him, noting the time. 'Do you normally get up at half eight?' Dan shrugged. 'Yeah, most of the time. Being out of work, people expect me to stay in bed all day or something, but I like being up and about. And before you ask, no, I don't watch the telly all day either.'

'Sounds all right to me,' I replied, picking up his mobile. 'Do you mind if I give World In Action a ring?' Dan said, 'No, as long as you put in with the phone bill when it comes.' I grinned at him. 'No problem,' I said and dialled the number.

It was possibly the quickest phone conversation ever. 'We've got a document with Prescott's name on it,' I said.

'I'm coming through,' he said.

I gave him my home address – my girlfriend would be at work, so there was no problem there – and I thought it looked better. Meeting us at another house might have seemed untrusting. Also, I did not want him knowing I had been kicked out. He might have wondered what kind of a guy he was dealing with.

We got to my house with time to spare and soon enough there was a knock at the door. Dan showed World In Action in, and I made him a drink whilst he read the Transco document.

It was a request for work to be done and was addressed to John Prescott, care of 'Wyke Property Services,' along with a telephone number.

As I brought the cups in, I could see World In Action reading the document intently, while Dan watched the television, only half-interested.

I handed the tea to them both, and World In Action barely noticed, putting the cup straight down onto the floor. It was clear that World In Action was fascinated with this piece of paper, his eyes were positively lit up as he read it.

I stood next to where Dan was sitting, and saw the dog out of the corner of my eye. I had completely forgotten about it! It had been sleeping behind the sofa as usual, and our voices had obviously disturbed it. World In Action was sitting in a chair next to the sofa and as he read away, the dog lumbered slowly out from its hiding place and headed for his cup of tea. I looked at Dan, he looked at me, and before we could say anything, the furry shit was snout down in his cup, lapping away. I expected to see World In Action look up and shoo the mutt off, but he was so engrossed he didn't notice a thing. Satisfied, the dog smacked its chops, turned around and disappeared behind the sofa. World In Action leant down, picked up his cup and took a sip. I grimaced.

He put the cup back down. He didn't notice, thank God! Then he stood up.

'That cup of tea tastes like a dog's buried its face in it,' was what I thought he was going to say. Instead, he said, 'I'd better be off. Ian, can you see me out?' He cocked his head towards the door. He said goodbye to Dan and handed him back the document. We walked out into the hallway and as I opened the front door, he whispered to me, 'Ian, I must have that document! Where did you get it?'

'You do know it's his son, don't you?'

World In Action smiled. 'Of course. Have you read "Fighting Talk" yet?'

'Erm...'

'There's no mention of what John Junior does for a living. Get me that document.'

'OK,' I said, 'I'll get a copy to you in the post as soon as possible.' We shook hands and before he left, he said, 'I'm trying to get you on budget. Did you get the expenses?'

I told him that I did, omitting the part where my girlfriend threw the envelope at me, when I dared to go down to pick some of my stuff up. I gave him the number of the mobile, and he departed.

'I hope he's going to the doctor,' Dan said, as I went back into the living room.

'He could have caught something off that flea-bitten mongrel.' I went over and looked at the dog, curled up and fast asleep. Obviously the strain of walking two feet and then drinking half a cup of tea had proved to be too much for it. 'He wanted to leave here with the document, not mange,' I said, 'Christ, it's a miracle he didn't throw up.'

'We should have had a copy of the document ready, really,' Dan said.

I agreed. 'Yeah, but he still would've come through. He wanted to see it real bad.'

We were all back at work in two days time and I wanted us to meet up beforehand and get something done in regard to this document from Transco. I rang around and, as Harry could not make it, Malcolm would be coming along. I hated that – Harry not coming meant Malcolm could, and vice versa. Talk about pathetic. Harry was acting like a prick over this and the next time we met I would tell him.

That night, we had another 'Cabinet meeting' as they were now being called. We would meet at a pub in the centre of Hull. We had decided on eight o'clock as usual, and Dan and I arrived there dead on time to find Jim stood at the fruit machine and piling in pound coin after pound coin. I went over as Dan went to get the drinks in.

He barely noticed I was standing right behind him until he hit one of the buttons, watched the reels spin and hissed, 'Fuck!' under his breath. He turned and almost smacked right into me.

'Bloody hell!' he exclaimed, 'how long have you been there?'

'Just long enough to watch you throw all your cash away. Where's Malcolm?' I asked.

Jim took his half-empty glass from off the top of the machine and we walked to a table. Dan joined us with two pints in hand.

The place was pretty quiet that night but I was still mindful to keep the noise down.

'I don't know where Malcolm is. I thought he'd have been here first.'

Just then there was a sound outside like a spitfire, followed by a thunderous farting noise and then a crash.

'Here's Malcolm,' said Jim.

Indeed he was. In strode Malcolm, dressed entirely in riding leathers.

'It's Mad Malc!' laughed Dan, as Malcolm waved then headed to the bar.

A moment later he was heading for the table, all smiles.

'See her?' he said, and we all looked over at the young woman behind the bar.

'She fancies me,' Malcolm said, sitting. 'She's staring at me, isn't she?'

'Of course,' remarked Jim, adding, 'because she's ordered a fuckin' pizza.'

'Never mind all that shit,' I said, 'check this out,' and I slapped the Transco document down on the table. Jim picked it up and glanced at it, then passed it along to Malcolm, who seemed a damn sight more interested. He read it, then blurted, 'Fuck me! It's got Prescott's name on it!'

'All right, silly sod!' Dan chided, 'keep it down!'

Malcolm looked around the pub. 'Sorry,' he said, bashfully.

'It's Prescott's son, anyway,' said Jim, 'not the man himself.'

'So?' I said, 'it's still pretty interesting.' 'We've already rung the phone number on it, it's a mobile and it gives two names; John Prescott and Simon Cutting,' added Dan, keeping his voice low.

That name, Simon Cutting, rang a bell. I had racked my brains until it finally came to me. I had played cricket against him when

I worked at a refinery. I was not sure at that point if he was part of the Cutting family who were in shipping. If he was, it would make things even more interesting.

'Anyway, time to open a kitty,' I said, and I felt eyes burning into me.

'What fuckin' kitty?' Jim spluttered.

'Yeah, Ian, what are you on about?' chipped in Malcolm.

I braced myself. 'Twenty quid.'

'Fuck off!' interrupted Jim, getting heated up.

I continued, 'twenty quid a week.'

'Fuckin' hell! What the fuck is this?' Jim moaned, 'Twenty a week? What for? Ian, we're pulling the odd document, that's all!'

I could see Malcolm agreed with him, and so I explained.

'We're going to be pulling a lot more documents, Jim, and we're using Dan's mobile as well.'

Jim pursed his lips. 'I'm not using his mobile, am I?'

'For fuck's sake,' I said, exasperated, 'just hand over the money.'

He sat there for a while, and then took out his wallet. The rest of us followed suit. 'I hope Harry's paying into this too,' he said, handing me a twenty pound note.

Fair point. I would have to go see Harry.

'What about you?' Malcolm asked Dan.

Dan was about to say something, but I beat him to it.

'Dan's already paid,' I said. He had not, but he had to shoulder the mobile bill no matter what, and as he was out of work he could sit this one out.

'Right,' I said, slapping my hands together, 'it's job time.' I was glad to change the subject: I had never heard such a hoo-hah in all my life. I turned to Malcolm first. 'Malc,' I said, 'get to the library, find out who lived at the house before Wyke Properties bought it.' Malcolm looked puzzled.

'Register of Electors,' I reminded him, 'and then look them up in the phone book; find out why they left the address.'

'Next, Dan, I want you to do a history check on the phone number on the document. Find out how long it's been active for and who's had it.' 'Jim, come with me to Beverley; we'll go see my mate at the council; he's dug up the planning file. We're going to go through it.'

I hoped Jim would have some sort of use. We could not politely ask him to fuck off out of it; he was in it too deep.

'We'll meet tomorrow at Dan's,' I said, and Jim asked, 'Why never your house?'

Malcolm laughed. 'Oh yeah, you're out on your arse!'

'I hope your bike doesn't break down, Malcolm,' I said, 'but then, you could always use your balls as a space hopper and bounce home, couldn't you?'

'Fuck off, Ian.'

'Meeting adjourned,' I said, adding, 'oh, someone read 'Fighting Talk', or at least skim through it. Find out exactly what it says about John Prescott Junior.'

Malcolm said he would get a copy and we left, each off to do their task. Jim would pick me up the next morning and we would all meet up that night at Dan's.

Jim arrived on time and we went to Beverley council office. Everything had been going smoothly but, as we drove down the road towards the council building, I suddenly remembered that my mate might not be there. And I was right; he was off duty, and he had not even told me. All that way for fuck all, and I could see Jim was not too happy either.

'Twenty quid,' he said, when we were driving back to Hull, 'you know, towards the petrol and...'

'Fuck off,' I replied. I wanted to see the planning file in person but I had a feeling I would not get to see it without help. I wondered if the others were hard at it, as I would have nothing to bring to the meeting.

Jim dropped me off at Dan's, and as I had my own key, I let myself in, made a drink and sat down. Dan was out, which cheered me up – it meant he was out doing what he had been asked. Around an hour or so later he arrived.

'Honey, I'm home!' he yelled, walking through the door.

I said hello and he threw a notebook at me. It was the history check on the phone number on the Transco document. I read it. The number was indeed for Simon Cutting and John Prescott Junior, at Wyke Property Services Ltd, and was shared with another company, Wyke Systems Ltd, formerly Alimentary Products Ltd., it would later transpire.

'Nice one,' I said, passing the notebook back. 'Are you busy?'

Dan shook his head. 'No, why?'

'I wanted to go round to Harry's,' I said. 'Give us a lift?'

Dan put his head down. 'Erm he's not there.'

'Oh, right. Never mind, I'll catch him later.'

'No,' Dan said, 'he works funny hours now.'

I looked at Dan. 'What? Why? Where's he working? 'Dan went quiet. 'I said I wouldn't say.'

This was intriguing. 'Go on,' I said, 'Where is he?'

'Shit!' Dan exclaimed, 'I'll take you to see him, but if he hits the roof, tell him you beat the information it out of me, Okay?' I could not believe it.

Harry looked up at me, then glared hatefully at Dan.

'You couple of bastards,' Harry shouted, 'why couldn't you leave it alone? I go where the agency tells me to fuckin' go, all right?' We were standing in a gentlemen's public convenience, and Harry wasn't a happy man. He was dressed in blue overalls and had a mop in his hand.

'I came here for a piss the other day,' Dan explained, refusing to meet Harry's gaze. 'Harry was mopping up. I'm sorry, Harry, but he made me tell him.'

'This explains it,' I said.

'Explains what?' asked Harry.

'Your house looking like a shit house, and this place looking spick and span.' I had to hand it to Harry, it really was one fine looking bog. 'You obviously take great pride in your work.'

Harry snarled, 'Have you come here just to take the piss?'

'Nah, I thought I'd leave some. That is the point of a public lav, isn't it?'

Dan spoke. 'I am sorry, Harry.'

'Why are you here, anyway?' Harry said, ignoring Dan.

'You owe twenty quid, for the kitty,' I replied.

Harry was not having it. 'For fuckin' what, exactly?'

I explained, and Harry nodded understandingly. 'I tell you what, Tony, my mate, he's got mobile phones – bulk buy, yeah? I'll get a couple off him, you can use the 'free time,' how's that?'

'Is that instead of or as well as the twenty quid for the kitty?' Dan enquired.

'What do you think?' Harry replied.

I agreed; the extra phones would come in handy, and we left Harry to his graft.

Dan went out first, and as I followed, Harry called me back. 'I work here two days a week,' Harry said, 'and I want it kept quiet. Please, Ian, don't say anything.' I promised him I wouldn't, and he asked how we were getting on.

I filled him in, and then I asked him if he had changed his mind about Malcolm.

'No, he's a lazy git,' said Harry. 'That's all there is to it.'

I tried reasoning with him. 'He's all right is Malcolm, he's just a bit zealous.'

'I want to help, really, but I want to stay in the shadows, I've told you!' I told him I understood, and he said he'd get us the phones. I left, and joined Dan at the car. Harry seemed so tired, so small, in there, and I couldn't help but feel bad about going there in the first place.

Jim, and then Malcolm turned up at Dan's that night, and all had something to bring except Jim and myself. I had to be there because I was living there, but as for Jim, he must have been bored at home. He was the first to open a tin, the first to give it some yakkety-yak, and he had done so little. Jim was always prone to talking the talk, and he could walk the walk too – when he felt like it.

Malcolm said he obtained a copy of 'Fighting Talk' and he had skimmed through it. He said there was plenty said about David Prescott, the MPs other son, but almost nothing at all about John Junior. He looked angry.

'What about finding out who lived at the house before Wyke Property Services bought it?' I asked, and at this Malcolm took a deep breath.

'I've spoken to them. They still live in the area.'

'And?' asked Jim.

'Their house was repossessed!' he said. 'Can you believe that?'

'Say that again,' Dan said, and Malcolm repeated it: the house was a repossession.

The room fell silent.

Chapter Fourteen

Malcolm was incensed, pacing up and down Dan's living room floor and ranting away. 'It's a fuckin' repossession,' he said. 'That company, Wyke Property Services, is involved in repossessions!'

Jim opened another can. 'Yeah, but just the one, like.' Malcolm rounded on him. 'There won't just be the one. We've found just one – so far.' He was seething.

'Hang on,' I said, trying to calm Malcolm, 'Let's find out exactly what's going on before we go flying off the handle.' Malcolm nodded slowly and sat back down. Everything else was put on the back burner as we thought about what Malcolm had just said.

I remembered that the next night Malcolm and I would be back at work together, and would have time to talk, so I asked Dan to take over from where Malcolm left off. I turned to Jim.

'Jim,' I said, 'you try not to get any lager on Dan's floor.'

He gave a thumbs up. 'You can count on me.'

Malcolm had left, soon followed by Jim and it was Dan and I who tried to piece it all together. Was this the reason World In Action had been in Hull all along? Not John Prescott MP, but his son, John Prescott Junior? Dan agreed that could be possible, but there were still questions needing answers.

'Tomorrow Dan, I want you to ring World In Action, ask him to do a search on the company Wyke Property Services Ltd.' Dan said okay, and I went to bed – as soon as Dan had stopped sitting on it.

I got up at four the next afternoon, with a headache and the house to myself. I felt bad about imposing myself on Dan's hospitality, but it usually passed after a few seconds, and as I lumbered out from under the blankets, I saw on the mantelpiece a couple of folded pieces of paper with my name written on them.

I read: 'Ian, have spoken with WIA. He has looked into the

company and has found the following: Wyke Systems Ltd. has Simon Cutting as director, along with a man called P.J. Jordan. He mentioned a whole host of other companies, linked with other members of the Cutting family, and this Mr Jordan appeared on most as director or company secretary. Moadvine Ltd.; Oakflag Import/Export Ltd.; Front Past Properties Ltd. Wyke Shipping Ltd.; as well as others.'

The note continued: 'John Prescott Junior was also linked with: Petroleum Clothing Company Ltd. and Wyke Systems Ltd., as a shareholder.' He ended the note with 'Gone to see Harry. He's got the phones and I've gone to collect them. Dan.'

I kept the note and sank back into the sofa. I had thought, a few weeks before, about how complicated the whole thing was becoming. It was nothing compared to what it had become recently. Later, we would find that P.J. Jordan was also Deputy Chairman of Pickering & Ferens Housing Association, and John Black was its chairman.

It was at this point that something very important and unexpected happened. I had been going to work during the week-nights, and sleeping during the days, and while the cat is away the mice will promptly go ahead and mess everything up royally.

Things had been going a little sour since Jim's apathy had set in. It was not the first setback – Joe and Gus had been the first obstacle – but Jim's cooling off was more serious than those two's antics, and one morning it reached its nadir.

I was on my four days off, and I found out that my councillor 'friend' had been blabbing to a local freelance. We were not pleased.

We had spoken to this councillor and had perhaps been naïve

to take him into our confidence, since he was now passing it on. We had to neutralise the information. How?

Like this: Ring, ring.

'Hello?' said the freelancer.

'Is that the freelance? The one investigating the council?'

'It might be, yes.'

'Do you buy information, 'cos we've got some info for you.'

'Oh? Perhaps, go on.' We knew he would pay us nothing.

'There's this little wog knocking around with a prominent councillor, and they're having a fuckin' good laugh at this other councillor.'

'Uh huh.'

'Yeah, apparently they've been feeding this guy a right load of bullshit. His name's something like oh, yeah, Ian.'

The penny dropped. 'Ian Newton!' exclaimed the freelancer.

Voila. Information neutralised.

But that was only part of it. The phone went, and it was Harry. He told Dan that Jim was saying that he was being ripped off by us. He had therefore rung a journalist, Dominic Kennedy of The Times, and given him all the names of the companies we had found. Apparently, while I was at work one night, Jim, the king of the swinging social scene, had gone down to Dan's and they had discussed everything. Plus, I had left my little book behind.

'Fuck!' I said. 'What a wake up call!'

I was straight on the phone to Mr Kennedy and I told him, 'This is our property, whoever rang you, the deal's off.'

It was pathetic admittedly, but I did not know what else to do – except ring Jim's neck. I had a few hours to kill before work, and I rang Malcolm. I told him to get himself and Jim around to Dan's. I was calling an emergency meeting.

'Why, Jim?' Jim hung his head. 'I don't know, I just felt left out,' was his explanation.

'You felt left out?!' I yelled. 'Kids feel left out, you daft fuck! You gave everything to a newspaper! What the fuck are you playing at?'

Dan said, 'That was really stupid, man.'

Jim looked at us: Malcolm, Dan, me. He started to say something, but the words fell away. 'I'm so sorry,' he repeated. 'I really am.'

Malcolm eyed him with disgust. Then he went for him. Malcolm pinned Jim up against the far wall and we all had to drag him off.

'You fuckin' idiot!' Malcolm hissed, one hand holding Jim up by the throat, the other curled into a fist. I was staggered; of all of us Malcolm was the least prone to this sort of behaviour.

'Easy, easy!' Dan said, pulling Malcolm back. 'Just calm down!' Malcolm let go, and Jim sat down, like a scolded child.

'You two have ruined my big moment,' Dan said, trying to lighten the mood. 'I don't know who's sent me them.'

'Sure,' I said.

'But it looks like they're from the Rates Office.' He took a large envelope from a drawer and slapped down a pile of papers.

'What's this?' Malcolm said, and we all looked down at them.

'There's loads!' Jim exclaimed.

'Better get on the fuckin' blower to The Times then,' Malcolm said to him. 'Fill him in on the latest development.'

'What are they?' I asked.

'They're repossessions, I've checked the lot,' he said. 'And they've got either Wyke Property Services Ltd or Simon Cutting on them. Now isn't that strange? No Prescott Junior except on the Transco document in Leeds.'

Jim and Malcolm's little slug-out forgotten, we all looked

through the documents together. They were exactly what Dan had said they were.

'I reckon,' Dan said, 'the reason the ones in Hull don't have their names on them, is because they don't want the clerks at Hull City Council knowing what's going on.' Malcolm looked up from reading them.

'They can't have anything to do with repossessions!' he said, incensed. 'Because of who his father is!'

Jim said quietly, 'It's not illegal though, is it?'

Malcolm glared, and Jim fell silent again. Malcolm was off again.

'You're right, it isn't. But it is wrong! Because of who his father is, he cannot be involved! His father is a Labour politician, and this is his father's own constituency! It's political blasphemy!'

Malcolm was right. This was where he came into his own: talking politics. Nobody was winding him up, taking the piss. We all listened.

'Look at it like this; you've got your house, you work for it, and then you lose that house, your home and you still have to pay the mortgage. Then you find out who's now got your home.'

Malcolm continued. 'It's the son of the man who's supposed to be backing you up in the Houses of Parliament. How can he be fighting your side in Parliament if his son is involved in the repossessions of his constituent's homes, eh? He can't.'

Malcolm stood in the middle of the room, his fists clenched.

Jim spoke again. 'Maybe his father doesn't know what he's up to.'

Malcolm fixed him with a glare. 'Do you honestly believe that?'

There was no answer, at least not one from Jim.

Malcolm stood up and walked out. 'See you at work, Ian,' he said and the door slammed.

I was still surprised; at the documents, at finally finding out what was going on, at Malcolm's impression of a bare knuckle boxer. The whole thing had just got even weirder.

'We'll have to meet up as soon as me and Malcolm are off,' I told Dan and Jim.

'Can you find out about all these houses?' I asked Dan. 'Find out which are repossessions and which are whatever?'

Dan said Okay, and Jim decided to leave. I was glad to see the back of him, quite honestly. He said so long, and a few moments later, we heard his car drive off.

Dan said, 'I can't believe how stupid he was. What do we do about him?' I admitted I had been just as stupid, asking him into the group in the first place.

'We let him stick around, I replied. 'He knows too much. If we tell him to fuck off, there's no knowing who he'll tell.'

'Cheer up, Ian,' Dan smiled. 'I've got a bit of good news for you.'

'Oh?' I said. 'What's that?'

'It's nearly time for you to go to work!'

I got to work, and who did I bump into? Joe, looking real pissed off. He said 'Hello', which sounded like it should have been pronounced 'get fucked' and I marched into the canteen. Malcolm was sitting in the corner, a table all to himself. As I entered, he sat up and nodded. 'You're early,' he said. Then went back to sipping his drink.

'Yeah,' I said, slipping money into the coffee machine. The drink popped out, and I joined him. He looked angry.

'I can't believe what's going on, Ian,' he said. 'He's fuckin' his dad's own constituents! He knows, you know.'

'You what?'

Malcolm scrunched his cup in his hand. 'He knows exactly what his son's doing.

Fuck legality! Fuck 'it's business' - we're talking about socialism! John Prescott is a socialist! Or supposed to be.'

I had never seen Malcolm worked up like this before. I decided
to let him get it all off his chest.

'Would you expect Arthur Scargill's son to have anything to do
with closed mines? No!'

'Maybe Jim's right,' I said, instantly regretting it.

'What? That he doesn't know what his son's up to? On his own
doorstep? Fuck off!' Malcolm got up, conversation over. He walked
out, and we didn't really speak all that night. I heard Gus say to
Joe, 'What's up with soft lad?' but I thought I had better not tell –
under the circumstances.

Two days later Dan roused me from my sleep with the news
that most of the houses were repo's. I knew what Malcolm would
say when he heard, so I asked Dan to tell him over the mobile. I
watched Dan speak and then hold the phone away from his ear.
Then he pushed the aerial down, the conversation over.

'He's pissed off,' said Dan.

'You don't say,' was my reply. 'What did you expect, exactly?
You know what Malcolm's like.'

It was not the best time to mention it, but I had remembered
who Simon Cutting was. He was the son of James Cutting, who
was the Managing Director of Anglo-Soviet Shipping Company
(Humber) Ltd. But, had not John Prescott professed to being anti
the shipping establishment? If he knew his son was involved with
this man, then it did not fit in with his image.

I was getting confused – the image and the real person? One
more night of night shift work to savour, and then it was back to
graft of a different kind. Malcolm had a face like that the previous
night, and I was sure we were going to have an outburst on our
hands.

Worse, I thought he might have said something to Gus or Joe.

I did not think he would do it on purpose, but the urge to tell someone what he knew and how he felt could have over-ridden the need to keep the whole thing 'schtum'. I kept an eye on him all night and he remained, thankfully, silent.

The final bombshell came at this point. I do not want to go into specifics here, but we fell out with World In Action. All I can say is it was entirely our fault, and had nothing to do with the reporter. One of us – not mentioning any names – had taken upon themselves to talk a little too loudly and it was all over.

I could not believe what had happened and I wanted to pull the plug on the project there and then. But Dan said, 'Keep going, find out.' His words were meant as encouragement, and I answered with an with an equally uplifting, 'Why don't you fuck off?'

Malcolm had a much better idea.

'World In Action must be about to make a programme, yeah?' he said. 'And they weren't bothered when we split.'

'So?' said Dan. 'So what are we going to do? We won't get any credit, we're left out in the cold.' He paused for dramatic effect. 'Let's leak it all!'

'What?!' I said. 'After all that shit with Jim blabbing to The Times, and you want us to just leak it?'

No-one looked at Jim, who was trying something different tonight. He was sitting and drinking a can of lager. Harry had come too, after I begged him.

He had gone into the whole 'but I don't want Malcolm knowing I'm involved' routine, which I swiftly countered with, 'What do you have to lose? You mop up piss two days a week. Calm the fuck down.' My sweet-talking won him over.

Malcolm explained. 'Right, here's what we do. We tell everyone – Prescott's enemies, the newspapers, everyone. Let's get Prescott.'

I stepped in. 'But Prescott hasn't done anything wrong!'

Malcolm replied, 'It's a betrayal.'

Harry sat forward. 'How?'

Malcolm tutted. 'You vote Labour?'

'You know I do.'

'Then you shouldn't be asking me that question. The people who lost their houses are the very people he's supposed to be sticking up for.' Harry didn't look convinced.

'Look,' Malcolm pressed on, 'his son's making money off people's misery, and his father knows about it.'

'Ah, but we don't know that,' Jim interjected, managing to tear himself away from his can for a moment. Malcolm was ready for him.

'If his father is the man he says he is – he'd have kicked the shit out of him by now!'

'Let's get him,' Malcolm continued. 'I'm fuckin' fed up with politicians conning me.' Dan said, 'So how do we do it?'

'Stick some fly posters up?' suggested Harry.

'Or we could get a plane to write it in the sky,' I said. 'Let's talk fuckin' sense here, lads. This is one powerful figure. He'll crush us like ants! And,' I warned, 'you won't just be taking on him; you'll be taking on his union friends, the Government, the media.'

Harry frowned as the room fell silent. 'How about we leave it?'

'No,' I said. 'All we need is a battle-plan. Pre-prepared defences. We have to be professional about this. If we go to the press, the journalists will want to print it, but the proprietors won't let it be printed.'

'Blair won't like it,' said Dan.

'Hey,' Harry said, remembering something. 'Didn't you meet

Tony Blair once, Ian?'

'Yeah,' I replied. 'At the Willows Club, when he came to Hull with Prescott. He seemed a pretty straight sort of guy.'

'What do we have?' Dan mused. 'We know his son is in with a shipping man. That's a surprise to me. We know he's also involved with a company that's involved with repossessions.'

'Did you know we're out of lager?' said Jim.

'Fuck off,' Dan said, then got back to the subject in hand. 'All of that is political suicide.' He put his hands under his chin. 'Now, think. How many people do you know? Your family know? Just by word of mouth we could erode Prescott's political base in Hull.'

Malcolm, who had been listening intently, suddenly spoke up. 'There is a way to get it in the newspapers.' His voice was excited.

'What? how?' asked Harry.

Malcolm smiled. 'We get Prescott to do it for us.'

'He can put me an ad' in at the same time. I wanna flog my mower,' remarked Jim helpfully.

Yet there was no denying that Malcolm had said something intriguing.

He continued. 'He must know people are looking into things by now. All those councillors we've talked to, they must've spoken to him by now.'

'Give it all to his political enemies, see what happens,' Dan said. 'Tell them all. Tell the journalists, the media, all of them – tell them that his son is involved in the repossession of houses in his father's constituency.'

Malcolm jumped in. 'The newspapers won't print it, you're right, but they'll be very interested. And sooner or later? Who knows, maybe it'll appear. No-one knows about the repossessions yet, so tell the councillors and they'll gossip like fuck.' Malcolm had definitely fallen in love with his idea. 'Prescott's phone won't stop ringing.' He laughed. 'We'll be talking to him, in a sense.'

And so we decided to leak it. All of it.

'Prescott's going to be real pissed off, you know,' Jim said. Now the booze had been depleted he had decided to join in.

'No shit? It's a politically sensitive issue, that's why,' Malcolm snapped. Jim sat back in his seat, contribution over.

'I have just one question,' Harry said. 'Who's going to go and speak with people? You can't just ring everyone up, you'll have to see these people face to face.' He was right. We looked around at each other. I felt a sudden sense of déja vu.

Dan nodded his understanding, then said: 'Harry's right. Whoever does it, they'll have to be able to politically defend themselves. I know I can't.'

I knew where this was leading, and it wasn't 'you sit back and put your feet up, Ian. Relax.'

'There's only one of us who can do it, Ian, and that's you.'

Well fuck me, I was staggered. What a completely unexpected turn of events.

I held up my hands. 'No way!'

'I know!' Malcolm said. 'Let's draw straws!' Was that meant to make me feel more confident? My success rate against straws was so far nil.

'Ian's at a disadvantage anyway. He's got a touch of the tar brush, so when he meets people they're all going to think, 'middle-east job' straight off.' I was touched that Malcolm would defend me, but I could see no-one else was having any of it. We drew not straws but strips of paper that Dan cut up. Not that it made much difference in the long run.

'No problem,' said Malcolm when he found out he had drawn the shortest piece. Then Dan said, 'Wouldn't it be better if there was two who went?'

'Tell you what,' said Harry, who was becoming irate. 'Why don't we all go? I'll pack us some sandwiches, we can make a day out of it.'

Dan took it on the chin. 'No, listen. What I mean is, it'd look better, more credible.' He turned to Malcolm. 'Wouldn't you prefer someone to go with you, Malcolm?' Malcolm shrugged. 'I suppose so.' And so we drew again, myself, Dan and Harry. Jim said he didn't want to, and we were not exactly going to argue with him. Harry looked at the piece of paper.

'Fair enough,' he sighed. 'Luck of the draw.'

'Erm… no offence,' Malcolm said quietly, 'but I don't think you've got the bottle for it.' Harry looked stunned.

'You what?!' Malcolm was certainly feeling strong lately.

He rubbed the back of his neck. 'It's nothing personal, it's just we talked about protection, and there's only one person here who can offer that.' Wonderful. Two draws, I don't get the short straw either time, and I still lose.

If only Malcolm knew what Harry had been saying about him – he would not have been so bashful in telling him he was not going with him.

I knew what was coming.

'Can't you go see 'The Abduls' in London?' Malcolm asked me.

He meant two Arab gentlemen I knew a while ago; one owned an Anglo-Arabic newspaper; the other was a press officer who worked at a Gulf State Embassy. They had limited power, but they both had access – and that was what Malcolm believed really mattered.

Malcolm explained, 'Me on my own, I won't be taken seriously, you on your own, you'd be a 'dodgy Arab'. But the pair of us together – we'd get listened to.' I could see what he was getting at and I agreed to go with him.

In the interim, we had something to do. We knew now that Petroleum Clothing Company Ltd had a 'voluntary arrangement' with their creditors, and that meant they owed people money. The company was insolvent, so one of us had to go to the Insolvency Service.

'I don't suppose anyone knows anyone who works there?' I asked, half-heartedly.

'Er leave it with me,' Jim answered.

'Just remember one thing about Prescott,' Dan said. 'He's a powerful man. Never play a game unless you know the last move will be.' Dan's face was intense. 'Anticipate. Think of all the possible outcomes and how to counter them. Think a million miles ahead of your adversary. And always keep something in your back pocket.'

DUSTBINGATE!

Chapter Fifteen

We would all meet that night at a pub, as Dan was getting a little sick of everyone sitting around his place and drinking his beer. Malcolm had been in contact, and told me that a local anarchist had heard about us as well as the repossessions (how did he hear? I had my suspicions), and wanted to get involved.

The story was that a group of 'Eco-Warriors' were going to occupy the repossessed houses and Malcolm had been asked if we could collect one of the protesters who was coming early for a look around. We agreed, and we were to pick her up outside a hotel in Hull not far from the train station.

'She's called Sludge,' Malcolm told me as we drove to the hotel in Dan's car.

'Is that her first or last name?' I asked, and Malcolm just tutted.

We parked around the corner from the hotel and saw a young lady already there, standing with her hands in her coat pockets.

Malcolm waved her over. 'Hop in!' he shouted, and she did so. We drove off, and Malcolm quickly engaged her in friendly banter.

'We'll take you to see one of the houses, it's not too far from here,' he said, to which she replied: 'Fine, but my flat's only two minutes away.' I looked at her through the rear-view mirror, and twigged. I slammed on the brakes.

'Get the fuck out!' I yelled.

She sat forward, and said, 'It's ten quid for hand relief, fifteen for a blow job, and twenty for straight.' Malcolm was flabbergasted. 'Aren't you an Eco-Warrior?' he stammered.

She thought for a moment. 'I can be anything you like. I think I might have a Red Indian costume at the flat, if that's good enough. But I tell you now, kinky stuff's extra.'

'Get out of the car!' I shouted.

'Yeah ' Malcolm bashfully agreed. 'We're in a bit of a hurry.'

'Well, I can take you both on at the same time if…' I spun around and told her to get out. She climbed out of the car and, before slamming the door, hissed at us: 'Are you a couple of queers or what?' Then she was gone.

'I'm not entirely sure what an Eco-Warrior looks like,' I said to Malcolm, who was still looking shell-shocked, 'but I'm pretty sure it isn't short skirt and high heels! Don't be so eager all the time!'

Malcolm said, 'But it could have been her!'

'Malcolm,' I replied, 'She had a fuckin' fur coat on! Point of reference for the future: if an Eco-Warrior tells you she'll blow you and give you change from a twenty, then she isn't an Eco-Warrior.'

We finally found her half an hour later. She had been standing on the opposite side of the road all along, and had presumably seen our little adventure.

'Are you Malcolm?' she said, and formalities dealt with, she hopped in.

She spoke as we drove, and she was certainly an upbeat kind of girl. She was into Nostradamus, the end of the world, and all manner of uplifting stuff like that. Part of me regretted picking her up – perhaps we'd have been better off with our first passenger.

We took her to see one of the houses then we went to the pub where Dan, Jim and Harry were waiting. She ordered a Snakebite and we got down to business. 'Right,' she said, 'where's the rest of these fuckin' houses?' I asked her how she and her friends would be getting into the houses, and she had obviously been studying the ancient art of the Ninja; move with stealth.

'Through the front window with a fuckin' Range Rover,' she replied.

Dan said to her, 'That's certainly a quick way to get the papers interested.'

'It's also a quick way to land your ass in jail,' I rejoined.

She sloped off to the ladies, and I told the lads, 'Don't give her any addresses.' They all just stared at me, but they always did that. She came back and said something that struck as me as stupid. Sipping at her drink, she said triumphantly, 'We've tipped off the police.'

'What?' I could not believe she would be so dumb.

She grinned. 'The police'll tell John Prescott, and he'll have a bad night's sleep.' Meanwhile, the houses would be crawling with Eco-Warriors and police, and the whole thing would descend into farce. We did not need that – we were more than capable of screwing it up all on our own.

Snakebite must mess you up badly because no sooner had she sat down than she was off again. While she was gone, I made the decision to stop the plan. Nobody seemed to bother when I told them what I was going to do, although I put that down to the fact that we were in pub after all, and all they could really think about was if there was any smoky bacon crisps left behind the bar.

She took the news well. 'You fuckin' wimps!' she yelled as she walked out.

Maybe the drink had made her bolder, but what she was proposing to do was potentially embarrassing to the whole Government, and we did not want that. The image of a Range Rover being reversed through my front window appeared in my mind for a moment, and worried me somewhat. We needed to know what was going on in London, and so we rang a journalist who was known to us, and who had an interest in Hull. His name was Christian Woolmer and he had an impeccable reputation. We rang 'The Independent', his ex-newspaper, and they had instructions to give his home telephone number should anyone wish to contact him.

The conversation went like this: 'Mr Woolmer?'

'That's me, what can I do for you?'

'We've got something to ask you.'

'Who are you? Where are you from?'

'Hull.'

'Oh.'

'Can you tell us, Mr Woolmer, if there are any Labour ministers who are having problems at the moment?'

'I can only think of one. Who are we talking about?'

'John Prescott?'

'Well, I need to know who I'm talking to here. What's your interest?'

'We were with a documentary journalist and we sort of fell out, and we know you have an interest in this part of the country.'

'Who? What journalist are we talking about?' We tell him the name of the World In Action reporter.

'Ah, yes, know him well. How are you involved? Give me yours and your colleague's names' – he could evidently hear other voices in the background.

'I'll ring you back.'

We decided to give him our real names, and I should ring him back. He had a good reputation, so we decided to trust him.

'Why do you think this minister might be in trouble?' he said.

'Does the word 'repossessions' mean anything to you?'

'Ah, yes! I have heard that a journalist has been asking questions about that. It's his son, not him. From what I understand, it's a councillor that doesn't like Mr Prescott very much and he had leaked it to a lobby journalist.'

This sounded more like Dan's handiwork than any councillor. We talked for around ten minutes and agreed to get together. Ironically, he was meeting World In Action the next day for lunch and to discuss some freelance work. He asked if he could mention our names to him, and we said that was fine, the split being amicable, and also for a contact number, which we gave.

By the Monday of the following week, the plan was in full force. Dan, who was in the thick of the local gossip, told us that it was going off the scale. John Prescott was not a happy man. Arrangements had been made to meet up with a local BBC journalist, and as this was the first of our 'open air' meetings, I wanted things to go smoothly.

Malcolm and myself were on our way to meet him at the Posthouse Marina Hotel in the centre of Hull, when the mobile rang. It was the BBC; the journalist was going to be late.

'You certainly will!' chirruped Malcolm before ringing off.

'Will what?' I asked.

'He said order the drinks and I'll pay.'

The man from the local BBC eventually turned up. He introduced himself as a documentary producer covering topics of local interest. All very BBC, I thought.

Anyway, drinks in, we got down to business. We explained that we were local researchers looking into various aspects of the sleaze allegations in Hull. He was quit a card this bloke and in between the talk, he had a tendency to slip in the odd joke just to keep you on your toes. We told him that, research-wise, we were a bit strapped for cash. We wondered whether the local 'beeb' would fund the remains of our research. 'About how much?' he asked. 'Two grand,' was our answer. In typical BBC fashion he seemed to go faint at the mention of money. We didn't want much really; perhaps Newsnight's bar bill for a couple of nights or Terry Wogan's annual toupée allowance would suffice.

We talked for quite a while, but the journalist would not part with a penny; it would take a shifting spanner to get a fifty pence piece out of this bloke's hand. He did though try to help us as much as he could, and pulled various documents from Companies House at the 'Beeb's' expense. We showed him a selection of some of the documentation we had and agreed to meet at some later date.

During the meeting, Christian Woolmer rang. I went outside to take the call, as talking to two journalists at the same time is the height of bad manners. He told me that he would like to visit Hull, and so I arranged to meet him at the Posthouse.

Dan had already posted Christian copies of the documents, and I told him to expect an envelope. He replied that he had already got it, and that he was very impressed with its contents.

I went back inside. Malcolm raced up to me, like a headless chicken, bawling,

'He's fucked off! He's left!' He was distraught.

'What are you on about?' I asked, trying to calm him.

'The bloke from the BBC! He's gone, and he hasn't paid for the drinks.'

Typical, I thought. We give him the documents – he laughs; we talk to him – he laughs; the bill for the drinks comes – he leaves. Malcolm caught the guy in the hotel car park and, to be fair, it was an honest mistake. He came back, paid and left – all the time laughing. We would meet the guy again, as he wanted more information, but not until after the media frenzy broke.

As we left, we walked past the reception area. Malcolm opened his mouth to speak.

'Don't fuckin' say it,' I admonished him.

'Don't say what?'

'Don't say those two receptionists fancied you.'

Next on the agenda was a meeting with the Yorkshire Post. Now this was an altogether more interesting meeting than the one with the BBC, especially for Malcolm. Alex Wood, the local reporter, was very good at her job and also, had a short skirt. Malcolm could hardly take his eyes off. As our conversation went on, I had the feeling he was regretting squeezing into his over-tight leather motorbike jeans.

It was like a replay of the BBC meeting: the same questions asked and answered.

We let them assume that we were gold diggers, because it made for a good angle. Poor people trying to make money off rich people is considered gold digging but when a rich person does just that to a poor person, they are an entrepreneur.

Anyway such is life. After an hour our meeting with the leggy Alex was over, much to Malcolm's relief I suspect. At Malcolm's insistence we remained seated whilst Alex Wood left first.

'Don't tell me,' I said looking at him. 'she fancied you rotten.'

Malcolm grinned broadly. 'You obviously noticed then. That skirt.'

'That wasn't a skirt she was wearing mate. It was a lampshade.'

'Well from where I was sitting,' said Malcolm. 'I certainly would-n't have minded plugging in my bulb.'

Happy with things we all met up in, of all places, a pub. We told the rest about how well our meetings went, but it was no use – we still had to buy our own drinks.

According to Dan, the 'Gossipometer' was now going apeshit, with everyone knowing two researchers were going around. Rumours about who we were working for was the foremost question being asked, and the best answer was that we were Secret Service.

We rang the councillor with the vivid imagination, or, as he was now nicknamed, 'Radio Baghdad' because no matter what he heard it was twisted to his advantage. We had ourselves an enig-matic little chat.

'Just to say I'm moving on.'

He laughed. 'Ah, back to London, eh? I suppose you'll be writing up a report to your boss?'

I tried not to laugh myself. 'Do you think I work for the Government?'

There was a short silence, then a chuckle. 'No, I think you work for A Government.' 'Whatever, I'm out of it. There's nothing more of interest in Hull. Everything looks nice and clean. You won't hear from me again, goodbye.' I rang off, counted to ten and then rang him back. He was engaged. Fancy that.

Chapter Sixteen

Dan had looked up who used to live at another of the repossessions, and it turned out to be a member of the Labour Party. He had been keeping an eye on it, and he told the rest of us that it had been sold. Who owned the house? A Mr S. Cutting, at the address for Wyke Property Services Ltd.

Dan had found out more. He said Wyke Property Services Ltd. were doing the conveyancing through a solicitor in Hedon, near Hull, but he would not say how he had found out. He had also discovered more houses going through, some of them repossessions. As well as all of that, he said that some of the houses were being managed by Housemartin Housing Association. Dan smiled. He said he had talked to someone there, who replied, when asked about taking over some of the houses: 'Oh, yes, Simon is very busy at the moment, and so we're looking after some for him.'

During one of Dan's little stakeouts, when he was accompanied by Harry, they saw a builder going in and out of one of the repossessed houses. Harry decided that they should tail him with Harry in the car, Malcolm on his bike.

Sitting in the car, talk came around to John Black and Dan said that Black was under a lot of pressure. He surmised that Prescott would be thinking that his own councillors were doing all the leaking in an effort to get rid of Black, who some of them despised.

John Black had come under a spotlight lately, yet he still held his position. We all thought it was because Prescott was protecting him. The big question was why? Dan said, 'Because he looks after the throne while the king's away.' Within the month, John Black had resigned as Housing Chairman and we anticipated a wedge had now been inserted between him and Prescott. Total paranoia now reigned at the Council.

The next day, the mobile rang. 'Broadsword calling Danny Boy, Broadsword calling Danny Boy.'

'Very fuckin' funny,' I said. It was Harry, messing around. They were doing their undercover surveillance routine again. I was barely conscious, having been working, yet Malcolm, amazingly, was already there. 'Where are you?' I asked.

'We're parked down the street next to the repossession,' Dan answered. 'Malcolm's behind us, down the street on his bike. Hang on.' I heard the car door slam.

'Harry's off for a paper. Harry, Harry! Get us a bag of crisps!'

That's it, I thought, don't let anyone know you're there.

'Sorry, Ian. Where was I?'

'Fuck knows, are you anywhere near the bloke's transport?'

'Yeah, we're right behind his van.'

'Not right behind it, I hope,' I said. 'He'll see you!' Dan went quiet for a moment. 'He won't! We'll be discreet, Ian, don't you worry.' I sighed. Why were they always so inconsistent?

'Hey, Harry's back,' Dan interrupted my thoughts. 'He's... oh, for fuck's sake!' My heart jumped into my mouth. What? He's what?' I said, desperately. 'He's only started talking to the guy!'

'What? The builder?'

'Yeah!' Dan exclaimed. 'They're having a right good chin-wag! The daft bastard!' There was a pause. Dan said, 'He's on his way back.' The car door went again. 'I'll put Harry on.'

'Now then, Ian?' said Harry merrily. 'What are you playing at?' I replied. 'Talking to the bloke you're supposed to watching?'

'I was only asking him about some plastering I want done.'

'Why don't you just take the guy to the pub?'

'Hang on a mo,' was his reply. 'Malcolm's here.' I could hear Malcolm talking about something to Harry, and the congested wheeze of the bike. Then I heard him roar off.

'Where the fuck's he going?' I said, and Harry replied, 'To the bookies. There's a filly in the half three that goes like the clappers, and he's putting the bet on for me.'

'I see you two have made up, then?'

'Ah, he's all right, I suppose,' Harry said, adding, 'as long as he runs my errands for me.'

I asked Harry what he could see, and he told me, 'A great pair of tits.'

'Pardon?'

'I'm reading The Sun,' he replied. 'Never mind about reading the paper,' I snapped. 'You should be watching the repossession.'

Harry sniffed, 'But there's nothing going on out there, Ian, only the builder in the front window. 'Ey up, leather boy's back.'

I heard Malcolm pull up, and then roar off again.

'Ah, good lad, he's brought me my betting slip.'

'Then the day's not a total loss,' I said, to no reply.

I was not impressed with their efforts at undercover and I wanted to tell them to ring me back later, when something interesting might have happened, when suddenly Dan said, 'Here he comes! He's coming out from around the back of the house, pushing a wheelbarrow.' A pause. 'He's even got a dog. Shit!'

I wondered what was going on. I could hear voices and then Dan whispered, 'He came over and asked us to move so they could get the van out!'

I shook my head. 'Fuckin' beautiful!' I said, craving more sleep.

Dan's voice still low, came over the mobile again. 'They're all loaded up. They're... hold on.' I heard the car start and I presume it was Dan backing up in order to let them out. Then he spoke.

'Right, they're off. We're going to follow.' Harry took the mobile now, and was giving me detailed descriptions of all the streets and directions they were taking. Fascinating.

'He's turned off down Garden Village,' Harry said. 'I can see Malcolm on his bike behind us.'

'Well, I didn't think he'd be running,' I replied.

'We're now north on Cleveland Street, and... oh fuck it!'

'What now?' Harry shouted, 'He's spotted us! He's... shit, he's off!'

'What?'

'He's doing a 'Bullitt' on us! He's off!' Harry was yelling this down the mobile at me, his voice a mixture of panic and excitement.

'No fuckin' wonder!' I shouted. 'He probably thinks your from the Social or the Tax Office! Let Malcolm take over now, where is he?'

'Er, he's gone. I can't see.' for a second the line went dead, then Harry said, 'I don't believe it! Malcolm's in front of the van!'

'How the fuck did he manage that? Was there a ramp on the road? Tell Evel Knievel to get his arse behind the van!' I thought that these twats would drive me to pulling my hair out. Only Malcolm could wind up in front of someone he was supposed to be following.

'Hang on,' Harry said. 'They've pulled into B & Q car park. They must know we're following them!' I could not believe he had the balls to sound surprised. 'Oh, do you really think so?'

'We're returning to base,' 'Don't bother,' I answered.

We all sat in Harry's, even Jim, who said he could not make the stakeout because he had been switched to days for a month. No-one believed a word of it, but we had let it lie. I doubt he would have done any better, although I can't imagine anyone doing a worse job.

Now, Malcolm, looking bright despite five hours sleep, was about to spring something on us all. He always read the local paper from cover to cover – from the weather to the sport. We were supping from our cans, discussing John Black, when it was mentioned that he was on the board of the Housing Action Trust (HAT), based in North Hull, which was set up with a Government grant in excess of one hundred million pounds.

'I remember reading in the local paper,' Malcolm said, 'HAT was advertising some houses for sale by some sort of tender.'

'What?' Jim said, 'HAT selling houses?' 'Yeah,' answered Malcolm. 'I remember it because it was a weird sort of advert.'

'What was weird about it?' I asked. Malcolm shrugged. 'Can't remember exactly, but there was something odd about it.'

Dan was sceptical. 'You're wrong, mate,' he said confidently. 'When HAT was set up property developers were specifically excluded.' He waved his hand dismissively. 'Anyway, I know some-one.' 'Don't tell me,' I interjected. 'You know someone who works there, right?'

Dan pretended to look shocked. 'How did you guess that?'

I honestly thought that Malcolm had got the wrong end of the stick, but there was no telling him. 'Then fuck the pair of you!' he yelled. 'Why is it always me that gets everything wrong?'

'All right, all right, calm down!' Dan said, trying to placate him. 'Here', he threw Malcolm another can, 'Get this down your neck, kid.'

Malcolm threw it down. 'No, you two always have to be right.'

'Stop getting excited,' I said. 'It's nothing, it's not important.'

Malcolm was full of it. 'Oh yes it is,' he spat. 'It's the principle.'

Oh fuck, I thought, here we go. It was now Malcolm's turn to throw a tantrum.

'I mean, just look at you,' he turned on Dan. 'Fuckin' big success you are, aren't you? Out of work three years, supposed to have all these mates.' Malcolm glared at him, his voice high with emotion. 'You're a joke.'

Dan retorted, 'I'm freelance, you shit. And you'd better watch your mouth, or else you'll find my boot in it.' Dan was serious – he had quite a temper on him, and I was surprised that he hadn't already started swinging his fists.

'Yeah,' Malcolm said venomously, 'A fuckin' freelance arse-hole!' Harry and Jim, booze buddies, sat in one corner, laughing their heads off. 'You tell him!' Jim laughed.

Malcolm rounded on them. 'And you two can get fucked as well, piss-taking bastards.' Harry said, 'Oooh, hark at him!'

'Go fuck yourself!' Malcolm yelled. 'All of you!' I went over to him, trying to cool him, but it was no use. It was my turn for it now. 'Come on, Malcolm,' I said, watching my words.

Malcolm stood up, ready to leave. 'No, stick your beer up your camel arse!' And with that he barged out, giving the door the most almighty slam as he left.

'That's what you get like if you don't get enough sleep,' I said. It had come as a shock to all us, what we had just seen. We looked at each other, dumbstruck. Jim said, 'What the fuck was all that about, then?' Dan hissed, 'Fuckin' loser? He's the loser!'

Harry asked me, 'You Arabs don't really fuck camels, do you, Ian?' 'Only after we've porked all the goats,' I replied.

The next morning I received a call from a nervous sounding Harry. He had got a call from our friend in the park, Terry. Harry was wondering how he had got his number. He said that Terry had heard on the grapevine that something was going on. He had asked Harry if it was anything to do with us. Harry guessing my feelings had told Terry in no uncertain terms to 'fuck off'.

Terry, we had found, was involved in a small business concern across town. Harry had scared him to death by quoting the name and mentioning Dan's. We never heard from Terry again.

Chapter Seventeen

By the end of the week we had all kissed and made up. We called a 'cabinet meeting' and had it at a pub in West Hull.It was disco night, so things were a little loud. The landlord cautioned us that if Harry and Dan were caught dancing on the tables again like last time, he would rearrange their faces. 'Have a good night lads,' he said, finishing his welcome.

We took a table in a quieter corner of the pub, by the pool table, and Malcolm, as good as his word, brought out a back copy of a local paper. There it was – the advert – from August 1997.

Dan gasped, 'Fuckin' hell, Malc', sorry mate. Looks like you were right.'

Malcolm smiled, satisfied. 'And you were right too, Dan, about private developers being specifically excluded from the scheme when HAT was set up.'

'So who changed the rules, then?' asked Jim.

'I'll have that talk with my mate at HAT,' Dan said. Then he added, 'You're thinking what I'm thinking, aren't you, Ian?'

'Well, we all know who's on the board at HAT,' I remarked.

'Aye, John Black,' said Harry. We all nodded.

'Right,' I said. 'This is one piece we don't leak. If we're right about this, we have to let the deal go through. If anybody gets a whiff of this and it gets back, they'll pull out.' We all agreed.

'Guess who I had a call from the other day?' said Dan, trying to be mysterious. 'One of the chief reporters from a local paper. Would you believe it? He asked me about you two. Asked me if I'd heard about you touting the repo's about.' This was cobblers. Dan had obviously rung him in order to put the cat among the pigeons.

'To tell you the truth,' said Malcolm, 'Ian and myself have already spoken to him.'

'Well,' said Dan, 'you want to be careful because they'll turn on you.'

'Fuckin' hell, don't you think we don't know that?' I said. 'He seems a nice bloke, sure, but it's the story that comes first. He knows what's going on, but I think he's holding back. We gave him a copy of the file, though.'

Dan grimaced. 'He knows your names.'

'So?' I said. 'In for a penny, in for a pound.' We had to shout the rest of the conversation, as the DJ, decided that you did not need to hear yourself think.

'Just remember,' Dan yelled, 'when push comes to shove, everything and I mean everything, names included, will appear in that paper.'

I yelled back, 'That's the whole idea. What else have you found out, anyway?'

Dan went into full 'journo' mode. 'The pot's really on the boil at the Council, and have you seen Prescott lately? He's looking really pissed off. Even some of the councillors have noticed it. As my old gran used to say, he doesn't know if he wants a shit or a haircut.'

We had all watched Prescott intensely, looking for any signs, any changes, anything to show we were getting at him. By the looks of him, we had been.

'What about you two, anyway?' I said to Harry and Jim. Jim pulled out a small wedge of documents.

'Look at this lot,' he said, placing them on the table. 'Petroleum Clothing owes money big style.'

I had a look at one of the documents. It was dated 8th September 1994. It was a report on a creditor's meeting held in Leeds for creditors to vote on proposals on ways to pay debts. We passed the documents around and all had a look, although it's hard to read by flashing disco lights.

'So they owed money in 1994,' Dan said. 'It's 1997 now.'

'They still owe money now – lots of it. Over two and a quarter million pounds to be exact. Now listen; one of the creditors is the Government.'

Dan pricked up his ears. 'How much for?'

'£312,861 to be precise,' said Jim. 'It looks like it's going to be wound up, only Prescott Junior jumps ship. He resigned on 22nd August 1997.'

Malcolm said, 'That means a few days with his feet up and he joins Wyke Property Services as a director.'

'He wasn't out of work long at all,' sighed Dan.

'What about the clothes they used to sell?' I asked. 'Do we know anything about them?'

'Yup. My brother's friend, he used to sell some of the clothes through the company's mail order side. Top notch stuff too, apparently. He's given me a couple of catalogues. All the clothes say "Refined in the UK" on them.'

'What does that mean?' asked Harry.

'Dunno, but I got Pakistani Pete to give Mr. Cutting a ring, and tell him how impressed he was with the quality and if could he get hold of more. Cutting gave him this line about selling the company name on, but told him the gear comes from Portugal.'

At this point, it was time for me and Malcolm to leave. We had an appointment with the local Conservative group. We left the pub and its ear-splitting sounds stating that we'd be back in time for last orders but if not, that we would meet back at Dan's. Dan looked overjoyed at this.

In the car I told Malcolm straight: 'no rolling up cig's in front of the Tories.' It would give them the wrong impression. On the way I topped up Dan's car with petrol and bought a pack of Berkley bombers (cheap cigarettes), just in case we needed a nicotine fix during our meeting.

'Fuck that,' exclaimed Malcolm when I told him. 'They can take me as they find me.' Malcolm admitted that he had never met a Tory before, at least not at less than egg throwing distance. I assured him that they were probably human, or at least the chairman sounded as if he might be when I had spoken to him on the phone and he invited us.

We arrived at the appointed hour and duly parked the car a suitable distance from the Tory headquarters, so they could not see we had arrived in 'a piece of shit'.

'For a socialist,' Malcolm said as we walked to the building, 'you're a fuckin' snob.

I reckon you're a closet Tory.'

'You just don't appreciate the importance of image,' I told him.

I pressed the doorbell and a figure appeared at the door. 'You must be Stephen,' said the man, and he introduced himself as the chairman of the West Hull Conservative group. 'We've been waiting for you, would you like to come in? My name's Reg Britton.'

We entered and followed him, me trying to be polite, Malcolm mumbling something about Stalin visiting Hitler's bunker.

We eventually sat at a large oval table, a big portrait of Billy Hague smiling down at us. 'Would you like a cup of tea?' the chairman asked, and we both said yes.

'Oh cheers Reg.' I answered for both of us. 'Milk, no sugar in both thanks.' I noticed Malcolm's little glare at the corner of my eye.

'What's all this fucking "Reg" business.' he whispered.

I smiled politely and whispered back. 'Just shut up, if you haven't got anything more constructive to say.'

Some moments later, he returned, cups of tea in hand along with two other blokes. They bade us good evening, and sat opposite us at the table, the chairman in the middle.

Chapter Seventeen

Both the chairman and one of the others were dressed very smartly, but the other guy was a bit of a mess. It later transpired during the course of the meeting, that he was a working class bloke who had made some money. His idea of social climbing was to join the Conservative Party and would you believe it? The first thing he took out of his pocket was a pouch of tobacco, with which he proceeded to roll himself a smoke. I saw Malcolm's look of smug self-satisfaction at this, and out came his tobacco too. Fuck it, I thought, so much for putting on a show.

Our meeting lasted longer than we had expected, and we never got back for last orders, but Malcolm and I were satisfied with how things went. The Tories had been very impressed with our documentation, and well understood the political significance of Wyke Properties buying repossessions.

'Them Conservatives are all right,' said Malcolm during the ride back.

'You've changed your tune.' I said with a look of surprise.

'Oh, don't get me wrong,' he quickly cut in. 'They're still a bunch of Tory bastards, but they weren't what I was expecting, if you know what I mean. That chubby one, he sure knew what he was talking about. Was he a solicitor or something? He knew the score all right.'

'The chubby one,' as Malcolm referred to him, said he would see David Davies MP to try to get him to ask some questions in Parliament. We had ended the meeting on a mutual respect basis, or in an unholy alliance as Malcolm put it. For the purposes of winding Prescott up, we would call a political truce with the Tories. We left them our mobile number and left.

Next on the agenda would be a meeting with the Liberal Democrats – and wasn't that a waste of time. I wished I had stayed in that night and done something more useful like clean my blowlamp. To make matters worse, one of them appeared to have grassed us up to the police, showing them their copy of the documents we had given them.

During the media frenzy, Hull's then only Liberal Democrat councillor would appear on local TV and say that she thought we were shifty and that she did not like the way one of us kept smoking roll-ups. That was to be her great contribution to the national Prescott debate.

Our next political port of call would be the local Socialist Group, known more famously in the past as Militant. The local leader had heard about our endeavours on the grapevine and invited us round for a chat.

Malcolm was Socialist Worker Party and, as there was a difference in political philosophy between the two, he insisted on trying to educate me as we drove. I decided to try and assist him with his explanation, by slamming on my Barry White cassette at full blast.

Arriving at the appointed hour, our host invited us in. He made us a cup of tea and we sat down in his kitchen.

All being socialists of sorts, and bound in the common cause of brotherhood in the struggles of the working man, it was not long before we knocking ten bells of shit out of each other in a political argument.

Eventually we got down to the business in hand and showed our friend some of our documentation. He spent the next fifteen minutes writing down some of the addresses of the repossessions, stating that he would try and get them checked out to see if they had had any grants on them from the local authority. He told us he still had some contacts in the Labour group and they were willing to have a look for him.

Coming across one of the addresses he hit the roof. He

explained that this particular address was the former home of a
Labour Party member, who he had personally recruited to the
party in the days when Militant was still part of the Party.

Throughout our little meeting I got the impression that for
some reason he had his suspicions about us, and this question
duly raised its head.

'What I don't understand' he said slowly, 'is just who are you
two. I mean, what's your angle?'

We explained we were just a couple of outraged Socialists. 'If
that's the case, how come I've never heard of you before?'

I detected the usual paranoia. 'I mean,' he went on. 'It's no
secret that Peter Mandelson and Prescott hate each other's guts.
I don't want to help get rid of Prescott just to help get Mandelson
his job?'

We both started to laugh. 'What, you think we work for
Mandelson?' said Malcolm.

'I don't know, do I?'

'Well, we don't.' I said.

We shook hands and left.

'We've worked for everyone now,' said Malcolm. 'The only
people we haven't been accused of working for is the Salvation
Army.'

'Don't worry, I'm sure we will be.' I answered.

'How did it go?' We sat down on Dan's couch, and regaled him
with our story.

'They're all fuckin' paranoid!' Dan laughed. 'Why don't you tell
Mandelson? Fuck me, that'd be a big bombshell!'

'Why not?' said Dan, who had taken to the idea. 'He's got an
office at Westminster. He won't pick up his own phone, but someone will, and it'll probably get through to him.' Dan slapped his
hands together. 'Fuck it, ring the lot up. Fuck the Lib Dems though,

they're not worth a fart.' He had made up his mind. 'First thing in morning,' he asserted. 'I'm going to shake all their trees.'

Chapter Eighteen

The phones were busy. 'Hello, Palace of Westminster.' 'Peter Mandelson's office, please.' 'Hello, Palace of Westminster.' 'Norman Fowler's office, please.' 'Diane Abbot's office, please.' 'John Redwood's office, please.' 'Conservative Party press office, please.' 'William Hague's office, please.' and on it went.

We were attacking Prescott on all possible fronts now; Hull Council, the media, Westminster. We watched him every possible moment, on the TV, in the papers.

It says in 'Fighting Talk' that he was considered to be a 'smoking volcano' and so we expected him to blow at any given minute and send the press after us. But that explosion never came. Instead there was a different development.

On November 5th 1997, on my first day off from shift work, Dan and I were sprawled out watching TV when we heard the rattle and pop of Malcolm arriving.

'I wish he'd get that exhaust fixed,' Dan said, recoiling from the noise.

Malcolm came crashing through into the living room, local paper in one hand, all of a panic.

'Black's quit!' he shouted at us. 'Black's quit!' We were up and attentive at this, and I grabbed the paper from Malcolm and started to read.

'Fuckin' hell,' I said, trying to read it as fast as I could. 'I bet Prescott's told him to stand down.'

I handed the paper to Dan. 'Prescott's weakening,' he said. 'Last week, the NEC suspends Black, and now he resigns.'

Malcolm, a bit calmer, sat down. 'Prescott can't defend him any more, can he?'

'He's sacrificed Black to take the heat off him.'

'You know what this means? It means we've sucked Prescott into a political game,' I said. 'And he's playing – only he doesn't know who his real opponents are.'

That night we all met up, at yet another pub. Dan had some news from his mate at HAT regarding the sale of the former council houses that had been advertised in August of that year. He was really excited.

'My mate,' Dan said between sips, 'says he thinks only two developers have tendered, but listen to this; he says he heard Cutting's name mentioned in relation to the houses.'

Harry said, 'Wyke's going to buy them!'

I asked, 'Your mate, Dan, he doesn't know anything else, I hope?'

Dan shook his head. 'No, no, I only mentioned Cutting to him, nothing else.' The information added up to something that made Dan angry. 'Can you believe the cheek of these bastards?' he said bitterly. 'All the shit that's flying around, Black's resignation, and what do they do? Bid for houses where Black is the vice-chairman! Now ain't that a coincidence?'

Harry chipped in. 'Maybe they'll get their bid rejected.'

Dan laughed. 'What? Of course they'll get them! They must be nuts to go near HAT in this climate of sleaze.'

Jim finished his pint. 'So what's our next move?' There was a long and thoughtful silence, probably because no-one wanted to get the next round in.

'I think we should take the heat off Prescott,' Malcolm said. 'Let this housing deal go through, and then hit him.'

'I agree,' I said. 'Give Prescott what he wants. We'll wait, because if this deal goes through, and we piss on the bonfire, Prescott will send the press after us.'

We all agreed.

'What about the reporters, anyway?' asked Dan. 'I had the chairman of the West Hull Tory Party on the mobile this morning.

He said something about a reporter from The Times wanting a meeting.' Dan looked guiltily at me.

'You didn't say fuck all to me about it!' I said.

'You were flat out on the sofa. It slipped my mind.' He frowned. 'Sorry.'

'Never mind,' I said. 'Which reporter is it?'

'Someone called Nick Watts. He rang up and I told him you'd meet him at the Posthouse Hotel on Saturday.'

'You'd make someone a great secretary,' I said.

On Saturday Malcolm and I went to the Posthouse to see Mr Watts. We were almost becoming jaded with meeting journalists now; it had become commonplace to us. We had been waiting for about half an hour when a kid who looked twelve years old walked in. He was carrying a plastic bag, which looked full of goodies. He looked lost, and I remember thinking, poor little guy, he can't find his parents.

'Hello,' he said to us, his hand outstretched. 'Nick Watts, The Times.' We shook hands. 'Would you like a drink?' Now there was an offer.

It went exactly as I had predicted; the same questions (Why? What's the angle?) and 'Here's the documents, enjoy, so long.' As we left, I noted Malcolm's rather solemn expression.

'What's up with you?' I asked.

'I thought we merited Dominic Kennedy at least,' he whined.

The rest of November came and went. My life now was work, mobile, read the papers, ring around, work. I had been home only a few times to be met with a Medusa-like gaze from my partner. She was still full of it, so I would just pick stuff up and then disappear again. One morning, the mobile rang, and I answered it to find a journalist, Peter Etherington, on the other end asking for

Terry.

For a moment I thought he wanted my erstwhile friend from the Direct Impact days, when Dan walked in. 'Who the fuck's Terry?' I whispered, one hand over the mobile.

Dan's eyes flashed. 'Me. I am.' He pulled a face. 'Look, you take the call.'

'What? Why?'

Dan said, 'I'm busting for a crap.' And off he went.

'Terry here,' I said, lowering my voice. 'Can I help you?' I came off the mobile as Dan walked back into the living room.

'I'm two stone lighter,' he said. 'What did he want?'

'He wanted to know 'Terry's' current assessment with regards to a certain councillor,' I answered. 'And I gave him it.'

'And?'

I sat down. 'He agreed with me.'

Dan chuckled. 'Great, isn't it? The Guardian asking us for our opinion!' We decided to go for a pint. I'm not sure why, but by the time we'd got to the pub, Dan had settled into one of his 'doom and gloom' moods, and the pub was nearly empty, which seemed to make him even more depressed.

'We've got to be fuckin' nuts!' he said. 'Prescott is going to fuckin' kick our arses!' Then he smiled. 'But you know something? I don't give a fuck!'

'Neither do I mate,' I replied. 'Neither do I.'

'I wonder if Tony Blair knows about what's going on by now?' said Dan.

'Of course he does. He's got one of the most sophisticated media machines in the world behind him. There isn't much going on in the party that he doesn't know about.'

Dan smiled. 'What do you think he'll do about it?'

'What – about the repossessions? Fuck all.' I grunted. 'If it doesn't come out, he'll just tuck it away, in his, "What-I-can-embarrass-my-ministers-with file".'

'You know,' started Dan philosophically. 'Sometimes I don't know why we bother.'

'The other night Jim and I, we were doing the pub quiz. And you know what one of the questions was. "Who is the current General Secretary of the TUC?"'

'So?'

'Well, do you know the answer?' he jerked at me.

I did not know the answer.

'Exactly.' he answered my silence. 'No one knew the answer, including me. Sad that, really.'

'The union days are over.' I said to him. 'They don't know how to rock the boat any more.'

'The union leaders are too comfortable. It's not that they don't know how to rock the boat. They don't want to rock the boat. All the fucking leaders do is pay lip service to the grass roots. If they play up, Blair just sends Big John to sort them out. "Come on lads," says Prescott, "get your arse on this committee or that committee. Drop in at number ten if you like and make yourself feel important."'

I laughed. I knew exactly what he meant. 'And then they come outside, all serious-faced and do a number on the telly for the watching peasants. We've said this and we've said that.'

'When really,' interrupted Dan. 'The bastards have said, let alone done anything. And Blair wouldn't give them the time of day. And you know what, I don't blame him, because it was them silly bastards that fucked the last Labour government. If they start with him, he'll just stick the political nut on them.'

Dan, like most of us, had always been a union man in his younger days. I myself had been a shop steward for short time.

As for Malcolm, his family history was steeped in Yorkshire mining traditions. His mother had also been a Unison convenor for years before she retired. So Malcolm never really stood a chance. Jim and Harry's philosophy was that unions these days were not worth the monthly subscription. As Harry once succinctly put it. 'That's about the equivalent of five pints a month.' And that is just about as cynical as you can get.

Christmas and New Year were non-events, apart from a few piss-ups, which we had throughout the year anyway. On one of these sessions, Roger Shrives of The Socialist newspaper came along. He had been sent from London, and we gave him copies of documents and had a long chat about the situation in Hull.

We pointed out to Roger a rather apt quote from 'Fighting Talk'. It was from the part where Harriet Harman was getting her arse kicked for sending her son to a selective school which was against Party policy: 'I'm not going to defend any fucking hypocrites,' Prescott had told an ITN interviewer. Roger loved that quote, and he would use it to great effect later on.

Then, on Friday 2nd January 1998, Dan got a call.

'Yes!' he yelled, punching the air. 'Yes!' He came back down to earth. 'That was a mate,' he said. 'The HAT board approved the sale of 18 former council houses on December 15th, to a local company called Wyke Developments.' His smile was from ear to ear. 'We've got them!' he grinned.

A moment later, he was out the door, and off to meet this mate who had 'some pieces of paper.' His last words before leaving were, 'Call the lads! It's action stations!'

By eight that night, the gang was all there – minus Dan who still had not returned.

'So where's the fire?' said Jim, somewhat irate. 'I hope you know I was on a promise tonight. Drink, curry, bird and bed. In that order'

'Our lass isn't too pleased either.' announced Malcolm. 'I've got a pile of ironing waiting for me when I get home and the bloody cat's got diarrhoea now. Fucking thing's been shitting all over the place. Right sloppy mess it made in the hallway.'

'Treat 'em mean, keep 'em keen,' said Jim, slapping down a six pack onto the coffee table. 'Put your fuckin' foot down.' No-one had the heart to tell Jim that was why he could not sustain a relationship longer than two minutes, so we kept quiet.

The distribution of cans underway, the front door went with a bang, and in raced Dan.

'Look at this!' he shouted. We all huddled around to read the document he had with him. It was marked 'confidential'.

In the document the HAT board agreed to the sale of the 18 (later upped to 25) houses to a company called Wyke Developments. 'Set of bastards,' Harry said. 'Look at the price!' Malcolm said excitedly, 'There'll be hell to pay when this gets out.'

'Yeah, but not yet,' I replied. 'Wait until they've done the conveyancing.' Dan said, 'Fuck that! I'm gonna blow it now!' He was all set to go.

Jim's voice had a tone of sarcasm to it as he spoke. 'Don't be stupid,' he said. 'They'll just back out, you dickhead!' Dan walked over calmly to where Jim was sitting and then blew his stack.

'You cheeky fucker!' He practically screamed, and before we knew what was going on, Dan had smacked him. Jim, more shocked than hurt, leapt up and the two started having the sort of fight you see in a school-yard, all hair pulling, missed punches and screams of, 'I'll fuckin' kill you!'

The coffee table went over, cans everywhere, and by the time we prised the pair of them off each other, Dan's carpet was soaked with cheap booze.

I grabbed hold of Dan, while Harry and Malcolm had Jim. They were glaring at each other and still struggling to get free.

'What's the fuckin' matter with you two?' I yelled.

'It's him!' Dan spat out the words. 'He talks to the press and he calls me a fuckin' dickhead? In my own home? I'll put him a wheel-chair, the bastard!' Jim, gasping for breath, struggled free and stormed out. Dan was still panting as I tried to find out why the whole situation had blown up, but he just yelled, 'Fuck him!' and that was the meeting over with.

'Does anyone want Jim's cans?' asked Harry, picking them up off the floor. 'Take them and fuck off,' Dan said.

'Thanks!' replied Harry, as pleased as punch.

Wednesday, January 7th. The mobile rang. Dan had gone with a bunch of lads to Liverpool to give some support to the dockers. The cap had gone around at work and we had collected a few quid for them, and the whole situation was pretty miserable.

It was Malcolm. 'Have you and Dan nicked Prescott's dustbin?' he asked. As conversation openers go, it was pretty surreal.

'Er, no. Why?'

'Somebody's pinched his dustbin. It's all over the paper, and he says his bank statements have gone missing. Prescott is saying he must have put them in the dustbin by mistake and someone's nicked the fucker. It's on Teletext.'

'Give us a minute,' I said and rang off. I switched the TV on and there it was on the screen: 'THIEVES STEAL JOHN PRESCOTT'S DUSTBIN.' I immediately rang Dan on one of the other mobiles.

'Have you nicked Prescott's bin?'

Dan started to explain. He had been toying with the idea of trying to make Prescott think that the mysterious Stephen had somehow managed to get his bank statements.

Prescott would think that this Stephen was a real hot-shot researcher and capable of near enough getting anything.

We knew from Prescott's land registry documents which bank held his mortgage and assumed he would also do his banking with it. Dan had rung the bank and had spoken to a lowly female clerk, ensuring that anything he told her would be a source of gossip within the bank, and hence give scope for a leak.

Dan had told the clerk that he had seen John Prescott's bank statements being waved around in a local left-wing pub by a journalist. He had then given a few days for the story to ferment, and for the bank to start its own enquiry.

Dan then tipped off the local newspaper pretending to be the husband of one of the bank's staff, saying that his wife had told him there was an inquiry going on into how John Prescott's bank statements had got into the hands of some undercover journalist. It seemed to have worked like a charm.

The local newspaper, it seemed, had contacted the bank and the story had been verified. John Prescott, it seemed, had told the local newspaper that he must have put some of his bank statements in his dustbin by mistake and his dustbin had been pinched.

This begged the question how, with police bodyguards stationed at Prescott's home, the theft could have been executed. The guards carried Heckler Koch machine guns and patrolled the grounds. Then there were all the other security gadgets that protected the house, video surveillance, infra-red cameras and laser alarms.

We all found the dustbin story a little curious to say the least.

I rang Malcolm back.

'It was Dan,' I said, simply.

'What?' Malcolm sounded terrified. 'Dan nicked Prescott's bin?'

'No!' I cut in. 'Dan played a trick. Made Prescott think he'd had his dustbin stolen. Listen…' I explained how Dan did it. Malcolm burst out laughing. 'That's fuckin' clever!' He laughed. 'That is really clever!' He was right, it was.

It was this event that truly started the ball rolling, although the couple of weeks immediately after Prescott's dustbin 'Theft' nothing happened. Then a London socialist rang to ask if a documentary journalist friend of his could meet up with us. Apparently, we had crossed into something he was interested in.

'What do you think?' I asked Dan. 'Reckon we should go?'

Dan said yes. 'He sounds on the level, but it's not me who's going to see him, is it?' Two days later, Malcolm and I were talking to this guy, who shall be referred to as 'Robert.' We showed him everything we had, and he read it eagerly. He said he had contacts, and by his tone of voice I knew he did not mean people who could get you a cheap stereo. If he could help, he said, we only had to say the word. He had access to a variety of national databases and his company would carry out any search, no problem.

Malcolm and I were hugely impressed by him – here was someone who could walk the walk, not just talk the talk, as we found out over the coming weeks. He gave us advice, helped us in other ways and to this day we are still in touch with him.

'What about Prescott's bin vanishing, anyway?' he asked us. We told him how this slight of hand trick worked and he too laughed.

'Fuckin' hell,' he smiled. 'He didn't fall for that, did he?'

Monday 9th February 1998. John Prescott Senior had a bad day.

At the Brit Awards he was soaked when an ice bucket was tipped over him by a member of the band Chumbawumba, who later said he did it as a protest against Prescott's perceived lack of support for the Liverpool dockers. Dan wanted to give them a ring but they had already gone off to tour Japan.

Next day, Dan bought their album. Pure coincidence, I am sure.

At work there was a shop stewards' meeting with a full-time union official present. Malcolm was our representative having been voted in at a union meeting some weeks earlier. He told the union official a little of what was going on, in a very roundabout way. The official said, sniffily, 'I have been in touch with Mr Prescott, and his son is not a company director. He works for an estate agent.' End of conversation – so the official thought.

Malcolm was feeling frisky, and challenged him on the repossessions. Just as frosty as the previous answer, the official snapped, 'They do not buy repossessions!' Then suddenly, from a corner of the room, another shop steward piped in.

'Yes, he does! My mate works for him! He's boarding up houses in North Hull right now!' The Union official snaps and loses it, refusing to discuss the matter further.

The rest of the evening went by more smoothly but a lot less memorably. On the way back to Dan's, Malcolm said, 'If he's boarding up houses, that means the conveyancing's been done.'

Dan was ready to see his mate, but I told him to wait until the morning as it was close to ten at night. He agreed, but I could see he was champing at the bit.

The next morning, my beauty sleep was shattered with the sound of Dan charging into the living room. He had the names of the solicitors who had done the conveyancing along with yet more documents. 'These are fuckin' state assets!' He cried.

'Morning,' I answered. He was fuming. 'We've got Prescott now, Ian!' he cried, slamming into the kitchen.

'Two sugars in mine,' I said, rubbing my eyes.

Dan shouted, 'I'm not making a drink, Ian! I'm looking for the rest of the documents!' I heard him crash and smash around the kitchen as he searched. He reappeared, and held the papers aloft.

'Who do you think will replace him?' he asked me, his face flushed.

'Replace who?' I did not know what day of the week it was.

'Prescott,' he snarled. 'When he gets kicked out!'

By the time we all met up again, Dan still had not calmed down. 'It's time to play "rope a dope,"' he said, referring to the old boxing expression. 'You what?' said Jim, who was as popular now as turd in a swimming pool.

'Rope a dope; where you let the other bloke knacker himself out punching you, and then you turn around and lay the fucker out with one punch,' Dan said, his eyes fixed with steely determination. Harry looked puzzled. 'I don't understand. What are you getting at?'

Dan said, 'We know there's going to be this media frenzy, right? Ian and Malcolm keep their heads down and so we make the press stay in Hull, yeah? Now, you're going to get slagged left, right and centre. Prescott's media machine is going to laugh and think, look at them! We've got them on the run! Not realising I've scattered the documents all over the place, ready for the journalists to use at their leisure.'

'What I'm saying is,' he continued, 'as it goes along, and with a bit of luck, it'll turn around on Prescott, and the lot'll come out. I think it's time we finished it.'

Malcolm went white. 'You mean, bring it all out into the open?'

Dan nodded. 'Yup. Let the media machine throw all the punches and then, when they think it's over, we land a couple of big ones right on his noggin.'

Chapter Nineteen

The mobile phones were now close to meltdown. 'Christian Woolmer, The Observer, Local Conservatives, The Times, The Sunday Times, as well as the local papers, the local Socialist group and, what the hell, the Liberal Democrats. We even tried The PM's office.

Things were now moving at lightening speed. We had met up with a local journalist, and everything was going smoothly. He told us he had door-stepped Mr Cutting and they had had an 'interesting chat'.

Dan was on the mobile as usual and told me something quite interesting. 'Prescott's been on to one of the local papers,' he said, breathlessly. 'He's trying to lobby it out!' This was his opening salvo, obviously – get the story kicked out of the local paper.

'What he can do, we can do,' was my reply. 'Get onto the Local Conservatives again. Tell them he's trying to get the story booted out. Then tell the Lib Dem's, then the Socialists!'

Dan had the phone in his hand, but stayed motionless.

'Just do it!' I yelled. 'Ring them!'

When he was done, I told him to throw me the mobile. I then rang Christian Woolmer, and we had a long chat. He wanted to give the story to a journalist friend, but he was out of the country. He told me he had now left the Independent and was writing a book about Stagecoach. This caused somewhat of an argument between Dan and Malcolm, as Dan liked his pub quizzes and he reckoned that Stagecoach was John Wayne's first film and Malcolm reckoned it was Randolf Scott's. I did not have the heart to tell them Christian's book was about Stagecoach, the transport company. They were both wrong it any case, because as everyone knows, it was James Stewart's first film as a cowboy.

No more than a second had passed when the mobile rang again. It was Jim. He was with Harry and they had been staking out the pub across the road from the Guildhall. It was a place frequented by local councillors and they were earwigging, trying to find out the local gossip on the political circuit.

'They're all saying Prescott's house and phone is bugged!' The glee in his voice was unmistakable. Jim then started laughing. 'It's a conspiracy theorist's paradise in there, and the beer's cheap as well. I have to go. Lord Lucan has just come in riding Shergar, I think Elvis is with him.'

By five o'clock that same afternoon, the main local newspaper broke the story. It made the front page, but it was not the main headline. We all had our own ideas as to why, given that it was the bigger story.

The mobile rang. It was Jonathan Calvert of The Observer. He asked for 'Stephen', and I answered. He wanted to meet, and we arranged it for the following Tuesday at the Posthouse Hotel.

I told him that the story had already broken locally, but he was not bothered. By Monday, he was not the only national journalist wishing to come to Hull. The word was that a few had begun to drift into the area, but it was the local television news who now turned on the heat. Outraged council estate residents who had bought their council houses appeared, and they were full of it, venting their anger at what they saw as the vast difference between what they had paid and what Wyke had paid.

Local property companies also appeared to complain about the price. As Malcolm commented at the time, it certainly made a change from 'vet's corner' or an interview with an ex-soap star.

One Hull property expert, was reported in the local paper as saying that there was no question that these properties were sold well below their real value. In the same paper, Prescott Senior said that he knew nothing about the deals, even though they had been approved by a regional office of his own department – not to mention all the times we had passed all that information to him via various means and channels.

The questions raged on.

At one of our meetings, Dan went through the week's events.

'Prescott's under a lot of pressure,' he remarked, and there was certainly no arguing with that. 'He's got to counter soon. He has to, or else he'll just go under.'

We had made sure Prescott knew just who we were – we had boomeranged him everything but our passports. We knew that he knew, and it was just a matter of time before he came for us.

Our local journalist friend was also giving us some highly intriguing information. For one thing, he told us that the creditors for Petroleum Clothing had been ringing up and putting the boot in, but Dan was unhappy with establishing a relationship. He did not trust them.

'I tell you,' he warned. 'When push comes to shove, they'll fuck us.'

Malcolm was in unsympathetic mood. 'We knew all along what we were doing,' he said matter of factly. 'Let them do what they like.' Malcolm was changing; he was growing in confidence. Jim was supposed to have been a major player in this, not the bit player he had become. It was another of the weird things about the whole affair: Malcolm, the butt of everyone's jokes, the weak link, had become one of the strongest.

Dan was awoken the next day by a call from Jonathan Calvert, who was on a train to Hull. Dan woke me, excited.

'He's on his way,' he said. 'And he's with a bird!'

'I thought it was Malcolm's job to think with his dick,' I moaned, wanting more sleep.

I picked Malcolm up from his house, which was in turmoil. Malcolm had tried to fix a leak, but unfortunately left the water running. Result? A leaking tap that had turned into Niagara Falls.

'My old lady is fuming!' he wailed, telling me he couldn't come.

'Look on the bright side,' I said. 'You always said she was after a shower.'

Jonathan Calvert arrived bang on time, along with his assistant, Lucy Johnson. To put it bluntly, she was absolutely gorgeous.

We moved quickly through the documents, and talked for around an hour.

Mr. Calvert knew what was what, and he was a walking lie detector. In fact, at one point, I thought I heard him bleep. He gave me a tenner for the drinks and disappeared into the night with the lovely Ms Johnson. All I got was the tenner.

Malcolm was still at home and was sitting, looking ashen. The ceiling had fallen in at his house, and surprisingly his lass was not best pleased. She had stormed out.

'All that water,' he said solemnly. 'It fell on her fuckin' head.'

'Do you reckon we should call the coast guard round to see if she's all right?' I asked.

Malcolm was not in a joking mood. 'She's gonna kill me!'

I took him back to Dan's where he managed to keep a straight face as Malcolm related his sad story.

'I'd make you some tea, but the cooker's fucked,' Dan said apologetically. 'Oh? Do you want me to take a look at it?' said Malcolm, trying to be helpful.

'Nah, I prefer my house with a roof,' Dan said.

There was an almighty bang, bang, bang! on the front door. Dan went to answer it and a second later he ran screaming through the house.

'It's fuckin' Prescott!' he yelled hysterically, and Malcolm moved like lightening off the couch and out of the house via the back door in the kitchen.

In strolled Harry and Jim, smiling merrily. Dan was laughing his head off.

'Where's Malcolm?' they both asked. They had just returned from the stakeout at the pub near the Guildhall. Half an hour later, Malcolm returned.

'I knew it was a joke,' he said, bashfully.

'Not a councillor in sight at the pub,' Jim said. 'But I may have a story; the landlord caught some bloke playing with himself on the bog. Shall I ring The Times or you, Harry?'

Harry scowled. 'The bloke,' asked Dan. 'Was he Labour or a Tory?' 'Definitely Lib Dem,' Jim said.

'Anyway, what was this bird from The Observer like, then?' Harry demanded. 'Oh, you know,' I said. 'About fifty, bottle neck glasses, surgical stockings.'

Harry tutted. 'Typical bloody high-brow papers. Give me The Star any day; best tits and racing in the country.'

The pressure on Prescott increased relentlessly all week. In the Hull council chamber, rebel Labour councillors mounted a full frontal assault on the property deals. As usual, the Liberal Democrats sat on their comfy political fence, content to watch the Labour councillors tear each apart.

By Sunday March 8th, stories in both The Observer and The Sunday Times concerning the property deals and Prescott Junior appeared. The Sunday Times also ran another story about Prescott Senior on the front page: apparently he had failed to declare a £30,000 donation. Prescott had simply forgotten to register the money, as he was obliged to do so under the MP's code of conduct. If we were cynical types, we might have thought that this was a 'non-story' put in by some clever-cookie Labour PR man in order to dilute the impact of the first. But we are not, so we didn't.

The Yorkshire Post the next day gave it the headline treatment: 'PRESCOTT ROW OVER SON'S EX-COUNCIL HOUSE DEAL.' There were now questions being asked in the House of Commons. And again, rebel Labour councillors were at it hammer and tongs, question after question was being asked. We anticipated Prescott's counter-attack – but we did not think it would come only a few hours later.

At about 12:30 that Monday afternoon, Dan and I were watching the local TV news, when Dan took a call from someone in London. He turned off the TV while speaking on the phone, and I could tell by his face that something was happening. He came off the phone excited.

'The Times,' he said. 'Its going to name somebody tomorrow.'

We needed to know what was going on in the Prescott camp. It was time once again to get crusty old Albert Gunner out of the wardrobe and dust him down.

Ring, ring.

'Hello?' 'Hello there, sir, it's Albert, sir.'

'I've told you before, Albert, don't call me sir. I've not been knighted yet. What is it, Albert?'

'Well, Sir, you know my lad, he's a good lad, and he works at a factory, you might know the one I mean, sir, it makes things; and he says there's all sorts of things going on about repossessions. It's all rubbish isn't it, Sir, it's all rubbish.'

'Oh! I know what this is about. Well tell your lad it's all lies, Albert.'

'I thought so, sir, I thought so. By heck, it's a bad business, isn't it, sir?'

'Well, Albert, do you buy The Times?'

'It's about one o'clock, sir.'

'Not the time, Albert! Put the phone next to your good ear. The Times newspaper, Albert, do you buy The Times?'

'Sorry, sir, I don't.'

'Well, buy it tomorrow, Albert, because they're going to name the bastards.'

'Oh, I will, sir. I'll tell my lad.'

'You ring me anytime, Albert, anytime.'

At approximately three that afternoon, I took a call. It was Dominic Kennedy of The Times. He asked for 'Stephen' and wanted to arrange a meeting for that Thursday. I asked him if there would be any cameras present, and he said no.

'*We* don't want to become the story, if you get my drift, Mr Kennedy?' I said.

There was a long awkward pause and then we confirmed the time and place for a meeting we both knew would not take place. I suspect that by the time he put the phone down, he knew that we knew what was going on.

'Who was it?' Dan asked.

'Dominic Kennedy, from The Times,' I replied. 'He's just tried to scam me.'

That night, there was the full 'cabinet' present at Dan's. Beers in hand, we all sat waiting for the midnight Sky News to review the morning's papers. We heard there was a Prescott vendetta story in The Times, but the reviewers did not elaborate. As we sat around, pissed up and philosophising, the hours drifted by, and before we knew it, we were waking up the next morning having spent the night on Dan's floor. In fact, I was woken up by Malcolm thundering in and tumbling arse over tit onto Harry and almost killing Jim in the process.

'My nuts!' he screamed in agony.

'Did you bring nuts last night?' Harry said. 'I didn't get any.'

Malcolm had been up and out, and had in his sweaty palms a copy of The Times.

'What time is it?' I said, closing my eyes as the living room light was put on. 'Half five,' Malcolm said absently. He was too busy reading the paper. Then he screamed it: 'It's in! It's in!'

Dan held his ears. 'All right, for fuck's sake, keep it down, Malcolm, you'll give the neighbours the wrong idea about me.'

Malcolm handed me the paper. 'Page ten,' he said.

'MONEY IS THE MOTIVE FOR PRESCOTT VENDETTA.'

The article named us, sort of, mentioning a secretive man called 'Stephen', and his evil assistant. Next to the article was a picture of a growling Prescott.

'They've just put that in to scare you,' Jim said, looking over my shoulder.

'Well, it's fuckin' working!' sobbed Malcolm. 'Just look at that face! He looks like he's just gone ten rounds with a grizzly bear and kicked its head in!'

'Ring him,' said Harry. 'Tell him it was a joke.' To try and prove his point, he started laughing but it was hollow, nervous; the kind you make on the way to the gallows.

Jim said suddenly, 'Fuckin' hell, what if he knows where we are? He might be outside!' We all looked at each other.

'Go have a look,' Jim said quietly to Harry.

'I've got a better idea,' Harry said.

'What?'

'You go take a look.' If The Times had intended to panic us, their plan worked. The next fifteen minutes was like a scene from the Keystone Cops. Five minutes later, both Jim and Harry had gone, not Deputy PM hunting, just gone. As Harry so succinctly put it, if he was going to shit himself, he may as well do it at his home. I grabbed my jacket and Dan's car keys.

'If the press comes knocking,' I said, heading for the door, 'you don't know me.' 'Know who?' was Dan's reply.

I sped across North Hull, with Malcolm behind me on his bike. I hit the kerb twice, and Malcolm took the wing mirror off a milk float. We had a bolt-hole, and we safely tucked ourselves up there; we just sat it out. Around midday, we rang a member of the local Socialist group, who told us people were asking for 'Stephen.'

It was all go from there. He said that 'Stephen' was getting calls of support from people on a radio phone-in and later, during the day, ITN news had featured Prescott talking about 'a vendetta'.

At half five, Dan rang. 'Your lass is going fuckin' ape shit!' he said, trying not to get me worried. 'She's got around twenty journalists and photographers outside the house. She says that they've even got a satellite van at the end of the road! You'd better get down there because she says she'll send the press round.'

'Did she say anything else?' I asked.

'Yes,' said Dan. 'She hopes Prescott kicks your balls off.'

'She's not happy then.' This was all I needed.

After I was finished with Dan, I rang the local journalist and asked him if he could give me a non-hysterical quote on how many people were really here.

'Just about everybody,' he said. This was much better. 'And,' he added, 'I'm under pressure to reveal my sources.'

Later, Malcolm sneaked, SAS style, out of the 'bomb shelter' and bought a local newspaper. 'THEY'RE OUT TO GET ME' ran the headline, along with a big picture of Prescott. The only good thing about the article from our point of view was that it mentioned the repossessions and council house sales. It was all fully out in the open, and a good part of me was relieved.

DUSTBINGATE!

By 7:30pm Harry had arrived. He tried to lift our spirits.

'You're fucked! Have you seen the telly? It's everywhere!'

'Haven't you got some turds that want flushing?' Malcolm said.

Harry let it wash over him like toilet bleach. 'They're wheeling out the locals to support Prescott. I've just seen Pat Doyle giving a sermon outside Prescott's surgery on the telly.' Pat Doyle was the leader of the Labour group in Hull.

To our anger, not to mention shock, we found out we were being linked with a break-in at Prescott's house, and so we made a decision: Malcolm and I would go to the central police station in Hull to talk with the police and answer all of these false allegations. We were getting a stream of reports of journalists knocking on other doors; Malcolm's door, Dan's door, and this made us realise that things had gone too far.

We arrived at the police station on foot, having parked the car some distance away. On the way there we had stopped off twice, to stash two briefcases. As we arrived, there were only two journalists and one photographer ready to meet us. We made no comment and, a moment later, we were inside.

As soon as we went in, the police tortured us – they gave us cups of hideous instant tea, but we bravely held out. They would not break us.

Around two hours later, the press outside the station had grown in number, Dan rang me on the mobile. He was very excited.

'Newsnight is live outside the cop shop! And that's not all – you've made CNN International News!' I tried to seem impressed, but I could not. We were called back inside the interview room for more questioning and, half an hour later, they split Malcolm and myself up.

Chapter Twenty

A detective sergeant and detective constable started on me. I was duly cautioned and the cops popped a cassette into the interview room recorder. They asked why we had come. I told them that Prescott had been on the box insinuating that the two researchers, namely Malcolm and myself, might have had something to do with a break-in at his house.

The two officers named the date of the incident at Prescott's house, and told me his mountain bike and a computer had been nicked from his garage. Prescott having a computer, I could understand, but a mountain bike? What also made me instantly suspicious was that there was no mention of his fishing gear going missing. Let's face it – when your garage is broken into they always take your amazingly expensive deep sea rod, reel and thirty foot motor boat.

I told them I knew nothing about the break-in. They then questioned me about the now legendary missing dustbin. It still had not been recovered and the police were still looking into it. It had simply bin and gone and the police were now waiting for a tip in their direction.

After half an hour, the two officers left the room for a few minutes and then returned again to question me further. Out of the blue the sergeant suddenly said. 'Where is the red file?'

Fucking hell, I thought, how does he know we have a red file? 'What red file?' I answered in some shock.

'The one in the black attaché case.' was his reply.

I could not believe what he was asking. How did he know all about the case and the red file? 'Are they at the address you've just left?' the sergeant went on.

'I don't know what you're talking about.' I said. 'What address?'

And to my amazement, the sergeant mentioned the address. All this time I thought, they had been watching us. 'How do you know all this?' I asked, staggered at their efficiency.

The sergeant seemed to smile. 'Your mate just told us.' he answered simply. 'What!' I exclaimed. 'Where is he now?' 'He's gone home.' I sat there absolutely stunned for a couple of seconds. Malcolm had really done well. In the space of five minutes he had told the coppers everything but the colour of his underpants; which were, I suspected, now brown.

I could not understand how the plan had gone so badly wrong. Before going to the cop shop, Malcolm and I had made the age-old pledge of loyalty and eternal friendship. We had entered that station a few hours earlier with all the bravado of a couple of drunken cavaliers. All for one and one for all had been the cry. In fact Malcolm had mentioned just before entering that he felt like Gene Kelly in the Three Musketeers, about to take on the world against the odds. Looking back now, I suspect that Malcolm had got his film analogy confused with 'Singing in the rain'.

The two police officers took me to the second address, which necessitated banging the door down at 3:30 in the morning so they could retrieve one of the briefcases.

The shadowy figure of the female occupant appeared behind the door. 'Is that you Ian? said a voice. 'Don't bang so loud you'll have the neighbours thinking it's the police.' The door swung open. 'Oh!' The sound of someone caving in Dan's door at nine o'clock in the morning was not the most welcoming of early morning calls. 'If that's the fucking coppers,' growled Dan. 'I am going to kick Malcolm's head in.'

'So what're you so worried about.' I asked him.

'There's no MOT, tax and insurance on the car.'

'Now ya' fucking tell me.' I protested at him. 'I've been driving the fucking heap for nearly nine months. I always wondered why I drove it everywhere you bastard.'

Anyway as fate would have it, it was not the coppers, but Malcolm. He was in a right panic. 'Two fucking coppers, one said he was Special Branch. The bastards rushed the house after they gave me a lift home. They turned it over like a couple of bulldozers. Our lass has just chased me out the house.'

'Well what did you expect.' said Dan. 'It may have escaped your notice, but Prescott does happen to be the Deputy Prime Minister. They are probably just looking for guns or explosives.'

'What do you mean!' protested Malcolm. 'JUST looking for guns or explosives! Why turn over my house. He's the fucking Arab,' he said in my direction.

'They obviously know something about you we don't.' I teased him. 'You're not a secret member of The Gay Liberation Front's military wing are you?' 'It's not funny.' scowled Malcolm.

'Anyway, never mind that,' I then started at him. 'What the fuck did you think you were playing at last night. I'm on police bail for conspiracy to burgle thanks to you. I spent half the fucking night trying to get my head down at The Hotel de Cop Shop with a load of screaming drunks trying to piss out of their cell door.'

I reminded Malcolm of the deal we had struck before entering; namely that if one of us got charged, we both got charged.

'What the fuck were you playing at?' I yelled. I was furious.

Malcolm explained that he gave the police the whereabouts of the second briefcase because there was hardly anything in it, just some notes and a handful of council documents.

'I thought,' he said, still in shock, 'that they'd charge us both!'

'So what? If the police see any notes, they might start looking closer at what has been going on.' I was stunned because Malcolm failed to realise this, which made me want to kill him even more. 'Brilliant idea, Malcolm, absolutely brilliant.' I sighed.

The local headlines that night said it all: 'PRESCOTT PAIR TALK

TO POLICE,' with a picture of a smiling Prescott.

'Has a nice ring to it, doesn't it?' Dan said, reading it. 'The Prescott Pair!' Jim joined in. 'Tomorrow it'll be "The Prescott Two." You know, like The Guildford Four or The Birmingham Six.'

'But those poor bastards went to prison for fuckin' years!' Malcolm blurted, panic-stricken. 'And they hadn't done anything!'

'You're always so negative, Malcolm,' said Dan.

I pointed out to Malcolm that as Prescott was smiling in the picture, it might have been a good omen, but Malcolm took one look and muttered something about starving tigers and hungry lions so I dropped the matter.

Also, Simon Cutting had added a new twist, by offering to sell the former council houses and give the profits back to HAT. Now if that wasn't good PR, I don't know what is.

The press swarm showed no sign of dissipating, and there were now a great number of journalists in Hull looking for us. Dan noted that we were still hitting the international as well as the national news, and it was clear to us that we would have to keep our heads down for a little while longer.

Watching the ITN news that lunch time we were the leading story.

'Well,' said Julia Somerville, turning to Michael Brunson, who was on live link from the grassy knoll outside the Houses of Parliament, 'is the government in crisis?'

'Well, it certainly seems to have put the issue of Labour sleaze at the top of agenda.' said Michael Brunson. 'And I'm going to say it before someone else does. Dustbingate!'

'What a crap name to call it,' Jim said, plucking at a toenail.

A few hours later, a journalist friend rang us to say that Jonathan Calvert wanted to talk to us. We discussed it and decided to co-operate. Meanwhile, across Hull, two journalists had found Malcolm's house and had shouted through the letter box at his lass, 'If there's any sex involved, we'll buy it.'

I rang Mr. Calvert on the mobile. He was already in Hull, at the Quality Royal Hotel in the town centre but he told me that it was full of journalists. I was to meet him at the front door, which was not the clandestine get-together I was hoping for, but I wanted to speak to someone who knew what was what.

Malcolm went home to change and join us later, and Dan dropped me off. It was exactly as Calvert had described it – swarming with journalists. We took the elevator up to his room.

We talked for about an hour, but Malcolm had yet to show up. When I rang him, he said that he had been intercepted by another reporter who was currently sitting in his kitchen. The journalist wanted to speak to the pair of us, and he asked me what I thought. Based on previous experience, I declined the offer and Malcolm hopped in a taxi and joined me.

By the time Malcolm had arrived, Lucy Johnson had arrived too. As he entered the room his eyes bulged. 'Guhhh guhh' he practically dribbled, and I wished he had been that articulate in the cop shop. We spoke at length for a couple of hours about our motives and about our politics, you name it.

It went without saying that Calvert had surmised we had combined research with a little mischief, but it was left unsaid. He had already done some looking into this possibility on his own.

We broke off around seven that night, arranging to finish the interview the next day. We taxied back to our bolt-hole and, on the phone to Dan and the others, I told them how much Ms Johnson fancied Malcolm. He then rang someone at work, and was told that the canteen was awash with papers.

Next day: 'PRESCOTT RESEARCHER SACKED BY BP' – Wrong!

'YEMENI BORN.' – Wrong! 'RESEARCHER COMPUTER EXPERT.' – Wrong! Phantom interviews were even appearing, making us feel things were getting dangerously out of hand.

Some papers were calling us the 'Men In Black,' a very popular term at the time thanks to the hit film. If anyone saw Malcolm walking around in a stunned daze, 'Men In Brown Underwear' might have been more accurate.

Back at the hotel, Jonathan read out some of the newspaper reports to us, and after Malcolm had stopped crying we concluded the interview. We all went for a curry and an hour later they had gone back to London.

The pair of us stayed for more refreshments and then groggily slumped into a taxi, which took us to a pub where Dan, Harry and Jim were waiting. As we walked in, we got the usual friendly greeting, 'What the fuck have you lot been up to with Prescott?' the landlord laughed. We ordered a round, and the landlord said, 'Have this one on the house!' and he laughed again.

For the next two days the newspapers chewed us up and spat us out – with unnerving accuracy:

'THEY'RE UNEMPLOYED.' – Wrong again!

'HAVE CRIMINAL RECORDS.' – Wrong!

'YEMENI PASSPORTS.' – Wrong yet again! The day after that:

'PRESCOTT RESEARCHER AND HIS MURKY IRANIAN LINKS.'

This story told how I had once met the Deputy Iranian Ambassador, who was promptly elevated by the paper to: 'The Middle East's top man in London.'

This was the card we were expecting to be played, and I knew exactly who had done it – my old pal, Terry.

We noticed with great interest that the story was not followed up in the nationals the next or the following days. We surmised that someone had hit the panic button in London. Stop! For fuck sake don't print that! Needless to say, it gave Dan another brilliant idea.

This local story had already upset some local Iranians. Like what is so murky about having Iranian connections? The local rag of course knew which word was mentally synonymous with Iranian, and that word is terrorism. Dan said we should try and wind up the Iranian Embassy by faxing them the story. Maybe, Dan said, we could get a diplomatic incident. We probably could have, but the rest of us decided against it. It sounded like one scam too far.

By that Sunday, we had our side of the story printed in The Observer. Our picture was included with the article, Malcolm and I looking mean and moody, largely because we were freezing during the shoot. The same day, The Sunday Mirror ran the headline: 'PRESCOTT SON AND THE £312,000 DEBT TO GOVERNMENT.'

We thought no more about the headline until Jim and Harry came banging on the front door. 'Prescott's on Frost in a minute,' said Harry all excited. Dan switched on the television. Sure enough, there was Prescott. He had just come on. He was angry about the Sunday Mirror headline, very angry.

Harry was shadow boxing Prescott's image on the screen. 'Go on Prescott, let's see what you've got.'

Prescott was almost ranting. 'Ah look,' said Dan laughing. 'Prescott's spitting his dummy.'

'Get him on side ref!' Jim shouted at the screen.

Prescott was now threatening to take a belt to the whole matter, whatever that meant. 'I hope he doesn't.' said Harry. 'With his luck at the moment, his trousers will probably fall down.'

We did not watch much more before switching it off. It had been one hell of a week for all of us. We had a couple of cans to help us on our way and got our heads down for some well-earned sleep.

For the next couple of days the odd story spluttered on in the national and local press. By then we were not taking much notice of them. If they had been any novelty value of being in the press, it quickly wore off.

As predicted, in an editorial piece for a local paper a few days later, the story was pronounced dead. Nothing else about Mr. Prescott would be printed.

We were all back to relative normality a week or so later; Malcolm and I were back on nights; Harry was still cleaning lavs; Dan was still looking for work; and Jim, well Jim had his hair cut last time I saw him.

I know what you are thinking as you read this: Why did we do it? You are wondering why I would choose not only to do something so strange, but why did I collaborate with people who, on the face of it, should not be able to find their dicks with both hands while wearing trousers with holes in the pockets.

But they could! Although we are pretty much working class stereotypes, we wanted to show the world that there's more to us than that. That was why we formed a union cell all those years ago.

I was born into a world of low income and poor job prospects – and what happens when you don't want to live that life? What happens when you look around and see the next thirty, forty, fifty years stretching out in front of you, and you realise you are trapped?

I, like the rest of us, wanted to live a different life, which is why we did what we did. You can call it childish, malicious, stupid – even, but it was an escape. Just for a few hours or days, we were free from the mundane.

We wanted to show that, in this instance, it was the repossessions and the buying of council houses that were the issue here.

It did not matter why World In Action were poking about, the subject was unimportant. It was just good (or bad) luck that it happened to be linked with the Deputy Prime Minister.

What had started as a shop floor wind-up all those months ago had ballooned into something close to an obsession none of us could let go. It was a bizarre mix of politics and adventure – maybe even, as Malcolm said, an opportunity for three factory night workers, one temporary toilet cleaner, and one unemployment statistic to change a little bit of history, to make a mark.

To us, John Prescott, the Deputy Prime Minister, was a challenge. We wanted to see if we could challenge him, as ordinary people, to test his metal against ours – his political philosophy against ours. Could we take him on and win?

John Prescott says he was always considered as a trouble maker in his shop steward days, because he dared to question. That is all we were doing. We took him on, and he came out fighting every inch of the way.

When we pushed, he pushed; as he lined up his allies, we lined up ours. The Housing Action Trust property deal was never the biggest issue for us, it was always the repossessions. Prescott says he did not know – well, he does now.

Let's see if he does anything about it.

The battle is over.

The Deputy Prime Minister, John Prescott is still there and we are still here.

We call it a draw.

DUSTBINGATE!

Contents

Introduction

In the wake of New Labour's landslide victory in early 1997, a group of five of us came together in Hull. We all had one thing in common: at one time or another we had been (and some still were) Labour Party supporters.

From the outset, we agreed to put politics to one side. Whatever our past or present beliefs, each felt he had been betrayed when trying to fight one struggle or another against authority.

It was time to employ the skills we had accumulated in the service of our own cause. We were middle-aged, disillusioned by experience, and working on night shifts and some of us were in dead-end jobs. At the same time, the local political scene was rife with rumours of sleaze and infighting. We decided to pool our local knowledge, connections and political experiences in an effort to investigate what was going on locally.

It was not long before the focus of the group's attention turned on the local MP and Deputy Prime Minister, John Prescott, and his eldest son, 34-year old Jonathan, confusingly also known as John.

It was discovered that he was involved in a private property company which was buying repossessed houses, not just in Hull, but in his father's own constituency of East Hull.

The firm where John Prescott junior worked was also buying up council houses at about £5,000 each. It struck us that this was not 'appropriate behaviour' for a family steeped in working class politics.

Councillor John Black, a prominent local political figure and a good friend of the Prescott family was vice chairman of the trust that sold the council houses. He was immersed in a sea of allegations in the local press, adding to suspicions.

Forgetting our pledge to put politics aside, we decided on an all-out assault on the Deputy Prime Minister using subterfuge and cunning to winkle out the facts. The political furore that followed was one of the bigger political stories of early 1998.

To add spice to the vast press coverage there was the mysterious allegation that the Deputy Prime Minister's dustbin had been hijacked. Thus, the episode was dubbed 'DUSTBINGATE' by some of the media.

The Great John Prescott Vendetta hit the press in March 1998 and for a while it seemed that the Deputy Prime Minister might be in deep political trouble. The Prescott connection with the sale of council houses at knock-down prices was made on Sunday March 8, when the story appeared on the front page of The Sunday Times and The Observer.

The Observer's account was headlined: 'Prescott son set to profit in DoE housing deal'. It suggested John Prescott's ministry had authorised an arrangement for the sale of the homes – initially 18 and then 25 – that would benefit his son although Prescott had been unaware of the transaction and his son's involvement.

The paper added: 'Although they (Prescott senior and junior) live together at the family home, he said they had never discussed the matter. His department only informed him after the decision was rubber-stamped.'

Prescott senior believed the criticism had surfaced as a result of conspiracy by 'his political enemies'.

He went on: 'There's a vendetta in Hull trying to link me into this matter. I don't put my hands in the pot, but I have to defend my son. It's a tragedy his name attracts this attention. The implication is that something must be going on. No smoke without fire. I resent it. All my political life is clean.'

But doubts were raised that a better price could have been

obtained for the 25 council houses. Westfield, a rival property company, said £5,000 was not a lot to pay. It added, 'If we'd known they were going for that price, we would have bought them ourselves.'

The Observer pointed out that the 'row' over the council houses was being fuelled by an inquiry into Councillor Black, described as a close friend of Prescott senior. There was also controversy about Prescott's previous business association with Simon Cutting, the head of the company that had bought the council houses. They had both been directors of Petroleum Clothing Company, which had been rescued from bankruptcy by a voluntary agreement with creditors which were owed £1.6 million.

The next day, March 9th, the Yorkshire Post picked up the story in a big way, headlining its front page splash: 'Prescott row over son's ex-council houses deal.' The story ran: 'Deputy Prime Minister John Prescott was faced with huge embarrassment on his home territory over claims that his son would benefit from a property deal approved by his own officials. Mr Prescott ordered an immediate investigation "to assure the public" over the sale of 25 ex-council houses in North Hull for about £5,000 each to a property developer and business associate of his son also called John Prescott.'

The Yorkshire Post explained that the Deputy Prime Minister had been dragged into the row after it emerged that that the Department of Environment, Transport and the Regions, which he headed, had to give permission for the sale to go ahead.

The houses had been put on the market by North Hull Housing Action Trust (HAT), which was formed to revive the run-down council estate. The paper reported that there were only two bids for the houses, one for a pound a house and the other from Wyke

DUSTBINGATE!

Developments where John Prescott junior worked as contract manager under 'his business associate' Simon Cutting. Prescott senior said he had order his Permanent Secretary to conduct an audit of the deal but he added, 'I am absolutely sure there is nothing wrong'.

However a rebel group of councillors was angered at the sale as it conflicted with an agreement between HAT and the Government not to sell houses to private landlords. Councillor Terry Geraghty was quoted as saying: 'I'm very unhappy because houses in the area have been going for anything between £20,000 and £30,000.'

The Yorkshire Post said John Prescott junior had once described himself as a would-be self-made millionaire. He told the paper that the houses Wyke had bought were derelict, requiring thousands and thousands of pounds of work before they were returned into the social housing sector for local people to rent cheaply. Prescott junior said: 'I have the highest regard for my father. I would never compromise my father.' He too said that people were 'after him'.

'With these very tenuous links they are trying to imply things, which is very upsetting and not founded people (are) trying to get at my father through me.' The DETR was quoted as saying that the tendering process was fair and open with no conflict of interest.

The same day, the Daily Mail headlined the story: 'The deputy PM comes out fighting over a tangled tale of two Prescotts'. It praised North Hull Housing Action Trust for transforming a 1930s estate of 2,000 houses where 25 had become surplus to requirements. Another Labour councillor, Anthony Fee, said there was public disquiet. 'My concern is that they (Wyke) have got these houses very cheap. We want to know how it came to be that these houses were sold for such a low price when the city council had indicated they wanted to take them back.'

The Mail added: 'The waters have been further muddied by the fact that the action trust's vice chairman is John Black, an influential councillor and friend of the Prescott family.' Black, it said, faced an unrelated inquiry. It reported that that the district Labour Party of Hull City Council had been suspended by the party's national executive committee. It 'is riven with factions and Mr Prescott's links with Mr Black have recently come under scrutiny.'

Again Prescott junior alleged there was a vendetta against his family. Everything had been done according to the rule book, he said, and the council houses bought by Wyke were not to be sold for profit.

The Hull Daily Mail got fed up with all the allegations flying around. It claimed that Hull had become the centre of intense scrutiny. 'The national and international media have been drawn to Hull by Deputy Prime Minister John Prescott's extraordinary allegations of against him in his home city.' A leader added: 'All the city's efforts to address its negative image will have been undermined by the events of the past few days – and their reporting from a London perspective. Having digested this week's national newspaper reports, outsiders will no doubt draw the conclusion that Hull is a backward northern city, riddled with corruption and racked by political in-fighting.

'It is a perception that has not been helped by the city's political leaders. Talk of the "enemy within" have only reinforced the false image of a political fiefdom rotten to its core. Amidst it all must be clearly stated that there is no evidence to support any suggestion of a widespread campaign to smear Mr Prescott. The combined investigative might of the local and national media has failed to uncover anything to suggest that the "vendetta" against Mr Prescott involved more than the activities of a couple of obsessive, conspiratorial mavericks.'

The Hull Daily Mail was referring to the next development in the story – the discovery that two local people, neither of them journalists or politicians, had been responsible for uncovering the sale of council houses and feeding the press with details. It seemed possible they might also have been responsible for a strange story that led to ITN first dubbing the affair 'Dustbingate' – the theft, according to Prescott, of bank statements and other papers from the dustbins outside his house.

The Hull Daily Mail now emptied page one for a story headlined 'Prescott Pair Talk to Police.' It said two self-styled researchers had been interviewed by detectives after they had walked into the police station voluntarily. On Sunday March 15th, The Observer devoted a whole page to the same topic under the headline, 'Small Fry in a Murky Northern Pond.'

Two photographs of Ian Newton and his friend Malcolm Parkes were pictured outside Hull's Guildhall. During the previous week 30 reporters had been camped outside their homes after they had been identified as the sources of the 'vendetta'. The Observer commented: 'It now appears there was no conspiracy or dark plot. There is instead a story of two ordinary men whose inquisitive natures and sense of mischief led them into conflict with one of the most powerful people in the land.'

It added that the two had been portrayed as 'shady malcontents' attempting to make money by selling smear stories. 'This is not true. Although the two men would like to write a book on the affair, they have not made a penny out of it so far. They have no regrets because their efforts have thrown the murky Hull political scene on to the national stage. The Prescott affair is seen as symptomatic of a council dominated by one party which is riven with back-biting, jealousies, power struggles and the whiff of corruption.'

This book is therefore the outcome of five men's attempts to shed light on the local politics of a major northern City. It is not an investigative book as it does not seek to suggest that the Deputy Prime Minister acted improperly. It simply seeks to tell a bizarre – and hilarious – story of how five working men, prone to bad language and a liking for alcohol, managed to intervene in the political process.

We hope it will be an example to others.

DUSTBINGATE!

Chapter One

The chorus of the song blaring over the factory radio could hardly be heard over the deafening din of the machines on the shop floor.

It was a song we had heard a million times these past few weeks and even though it was getting to be a little monotonous, the whole of the night shift joined in with the words: 'Things can only get better! Can only get better!' 'Yeah! We're gonna fuck the Tories!' Joe yelled over the blare of the music. He was practically dancing around, like a jubilant boxer who'd just floored his opponent. Anyone who knew Joe knew that for him to move like that would take a pretty special occasion – and tonight was one. Eighteen years of Conservative leadership was finally coming to an end – we could feel it.

'Never mind fucking the Tories, Joe,' interrupted Jeff, the night shift team manager, 'Just make sure that machine keeps going. If the figures go down it'll be you who's getting fucked!' With that, everyone settled down again and tried to get back into the routine of the job. There were five of us on the orange team night shift and, barring Nick, who was a temporary worker, we all got on like a house on fire. The working week was forty-eight hours, over four nights and if you don't see eye-to-eye with those you work with, it can be a right pain. We covered each other's backs, making sure that any problems we had with each other stayed firmly within the group. We had all been at the factory for around two years, except Joe, who started just after us.

Joe had been out of work for a fair few years before getting a job at the factory.

He had worked at a local brewery before that, and he had seen the good and the bad times of Hull's fluctuating fortunes. All Joe had now was his beloved Labour Party and his equally beloved rugby team, the Hull Sharks.

DUSTBINGATE!

We had all been on the dole before starting at the factory and although it wasn't the best job in the world, it beat signing on hands down. It was knackering work, and not the most mentally challenging of vocations; you worked like a mule, with the constant roar of the machines in your ears. Your mind would wander and you'd find yourself daydreaming and before you knew it, management would be walking over, telling you to 'get your arse in gear'. The cherry on the top was the little peaked cap you had to wear. Still, if you were prepared to graft there was some good money to be made.

It was about three or four in the morning when we really knew the Tories were finished. Someone had tuned one of the radios to Radio 4 and our spirits rose as we heard the results coming in. Gus, one of our team, was as high as a kite, singing and laughing. When it was time for our break, we all went into the canteen.

It was empty when we got there and so we proceeded to have a little celebration of our own. We couldn't believe it when Gus sloped off and came back with five cups of coffee. The guy was usually as tight as a mouse's ring piece.

Gus passed the cups around. There was Gus, Joe, Nick and Matthew and myself. Matthew was always going on about politics, more so than Gus and Joe put together, and he would bang on about all the shit the politicians got up to and how he knew what the country needed, if only anyone would just listen to him for five minutes. He was a real social idealist and pretty naive to boot.

Joe was beaming. 'Fuckin' beautiful!' he laughed. He took a sip of his coffee and wiped his mouth. 'I can't believe it! I honestly can't!'

'You and me both,' said Gus. He too, was grinning away.

'Keep it down, eh, lads?' said Malcolm in a half-whisper. 'If the management find us sitting around having a knees-up we're fucked.'

'Yeah, Malcolm's right,' I said, remembering that, Labour victory or no Labour victory, having too good a time on night shift was a major no-no. 'I don't want to be dunked in the shit tonight of all nights! We could all get the chop and I don't fancy being the first bloke to sign on under Labour, all right?'

This seemed to sink in and the row settled down in volume. I was as happy as the rest of them of course, but I was also mindful not only of the management, but also of the grasses that would just love to see what we were up to and blow the whistle. I knew Nick had a big mouth when it came to telling the bosses what went on, so I was always careful what I said and did in front of him. There's more backbiting going on in factories than in any other workplace in the world. Still, I didn't like having to tell everyone to keep it down.

My memory of that night gets a little hazy, but I can vaguely remember Gus getting very upset because he went off to the toilet and when he came back someone had eaten the pork pie he'd been saving especially for the big night. He swore blind that Joe was the guilty party, but Joe's cries of denial were deafening. It's a wonder no-one heard Gus and Joe's barney, and I can remember thinking that we were all going to get the sack all because of a pork pie. It's typical of working in a factory: one moment it's in-depth political analysis and the next someone is pissing and moaning because someone has eaten his pork pie while he was on the bog.

Finally, 6am came around and everyone piled out into the cool breeze of the morning, feeling like we owned the world. Gus said he had a fridge full of booze at home and that we were all welcome to go back with him and continue the festivities. He didn't exactly have to do any arm-twisting and soon we were sat in his house, feet up, drink in hand, watching the news and having a right good laugh. I got home just after 9:30am, happy as hell. It was true - Labour had won. Tony Blair was the new Prime Minister. Satisfied, I went to bed.

I got up that day at three in the afternoon – one hour before I normally do on a work day, because I wanted time to watch the TV without having to rush. Sitting there, watching Blair walk into Number 10 was incredible. It felt like Christmas, and as soon as I got to work I knew exactly what I'd get as soon as I walked through the door. The first person to come up to me was Gus who was all smiles. He's a big bastard is Gus, with great big mutton-chop side-boards which hung off his face. We called him 'The British Bulldog' because of it, which he took with a good sense of humour. Good job too, as he could have knocked the shite out of all of us with one punch.

'Now then, Ian,' he grinned, 'what a night, eh? Eighteen fucking years! But I'm telling you, it's worth the wait, innit?' 'Yeah,' I replied, as I saw the other three go into the full canteen, already togged up. 'I knew you'd be over the moon.' Gus pretended to look aghast. 'What and you're not? Fuck off, Ian! You're worse than I am when you get started, you bolshie bastard!' He pulled his hat out of his overall pocket and put it on his head. 'You know, this is the first time since I've started here that I don't mind wearing this for once.' He turned and walked off in the direction of the canteen. To men like Gus the thought of the Tories being kicked out was better than winning the lottery. I got changed and followed.

The canteen was always buzzing at the beginning of the shift but tonight the place looked like a library. Newspapers were strewn all over the tables and there was only one topic of conversation. It was almost as noisy as the shop floor and as I entered,

Gus shouted over to me. 'Oi! Ian! Over here! We've saved you a seat!' I made my way through the groups of people to a table at the back of the room. As usual, there was Gus, Joe, Nick and Malcolm already seated. It was no surprise what Malcolm spoke about – it was probably the only thing he and the others had thought about all day.

'Seen the news today, Ian?' he began. A snort of derision erupted from Nick. 'Of course he's seen the bloody news, he hasn't had his head down a hole.' Joe chimed in, all smiles. 'Here, read the papers – it was a massacre!' I've seldom seen anyone look so happy in all my life.

Malcolm did his political doomsayer bit. 'It wasn't that big a victory. People were voting against the Tories, not for Labour.' He sat back, a small smile on his face.

'For fuck's sake, can't you just be happy for us?' Joe snapped, exasperated.

'Aye, shut up, Mr Socialist Worker Party,' sniped Gus, 'just because you want to burn down the Houses of Parliament with all of `em in it.'

Malcolm pulled a face. He held some pretty left wing views, which were seen by the others as laughable. Whenever the shit flew in a row, and nine times out of ten, the barbs would head straight in Malcolm's direction for being a 'Loony Lefty'. Tonight was looking like it might be one of those nights.

Malcolm threw his hands up in defence.

'I'm just saying, like, Blair – he'll turn out to be as bad as Major. I've seen him talking.'

'Bollocks, it is!' Joe sat up quickly in order to rise to the challenge.

'Christ, he's barely had time to fuckin' brew up in Number Ten and you want him out.' Malcolm looked to me for back-up but I was staying out of it. I was still feeling shagged out from the night before and the last thing I wanted was a big debate as soon as I sat down. 'Red Ted rides again!' laughed Gus. Nick laughed too, and Malcolm fell silent.

'Look,' said Nick, 'I don't give a flying fuck who's in the driving seat normally, but even I know that Blair's a better bet than Major.'

'You should be happy, like the rest of us.' agreed Joe.

'You just wait,' said Malcolm, 'As soon as he's got his feet under the table he'll be in with all the big-wigs and it'll be friggin' champagne and strawberries all the way.'

'Look,' Joe said, leaning over the table, 'I know he's got his faults, but he'll do all right.'

'Yeah, but Blair's got one big fault,' said Nick.

Now, when Nick finally used to talk, it was usually to slag some-one off. He never had a good word to say about anyone. He continued: 'What's-his-face, Prescott.' With this, the group seemed to prick up their ears.

'Go on. What's he done to you then?' said Malcolm.

Nick shrugged. 'Fuck all. But there's some pretty interesting stuff going around about what he's been up to; especially with Black.' Nick was right, there were rumours circulating about Hull Councillor John Black and Hull Labour MP John Prescott. But they were all a little vague and non-specific. Still, people love to talk.

'Where did you hear all this, then?' I asked.

'Well, my brother's friend's missus, right, she cleans at the council offices, and...'

'Oh, well, that's all right then,' I cut in, 'you got it off your third cousin's wife's sister's auntie. Fuckin' hell, who needs Newsnight?' I really couldn't keep it in. But then he said something that was intriguing.

'There's a bloke knocking around from World in Action, yeah?

I don't know what he's looking into, but it wouldn't surprise me if it has something to do with all the shit that's been flying about.'

This last part was the most interesting. Why would someone make up such a story? Nick had an attentive audience now, and that seemed to hit his stride. 'All I know is that. But it's pretty interesting, innit?'

The clock on the canteen wall was near enough eight, and people began swarming out onto the shop floor. Gus and Malcolm went out first, followed by Joe. As I rose, Nick turned to me and said, 'I bet you he's up to all sorts, that Prescott. You mark my words.' What Nick had just said was, in many ways, typical idle factory gossip, spoken by bored workers eager to have something to say that'll make you sit up and listen. By the time a rumour finishes circulating, it's a hundred times more amazing than it was when it started. But still, why had someone thrown World In Action specifically into the story?

It all seemed a bit too precise to be just made-up bullshit. I walked out of the canteen thinking it over. It was not as if the job would occupy my mind instead. It was certainly a fascinating tale, and in a few days time, something would happen that would make it a whole lot more fascinating.

DUSTBINGATE!

Chapter Two

I emerged from bed at around four o'clock in the afternoon the next day. Today was the beginning of the shift's four days off. I work shifts primarily because I hate getting up in the morning; nine-to-five is a big problem for me; always has been.

As usual, I felt absolutely knackered after the last four nights and I knew I would feel like this until Saturday at the earliest. Still, it was always good to be shot of work for a few days, and the recent political events had me in a better mood than I normally would be on my first day off.

My partner would not be home from work for at least another hour, which gave me some time to laze around in my pyjamas and dressing gown, which is something that always infuriates her for some reason. Working nights tend to make you want to please yourself when you do get some free time, but she thinks I'm a lazy bastard who works with a group of other lazy bastards. Sometimes it's hard not to shout out that I've just come off a forty-eight hour working week that's been compressed into four nights, but when I think I'm about to blow, I'm invariably laid on the couch in a dressing gown smoking a roll-up. She's a very perceptive woman, now I think about it.

I rolled myself a fag. Until I started at the factory I always smoked cigarettes but roll-ups were a lot cheaper and Joe sold tobacco on the side at a reduced rate. The tobacco was smuggled into the country and Malcolm took great pleasure in telling us that those of us from the factory who smoked it were ripping the government off to the tune of something like three hundred quid a week. Malcolm liked working things like that out, and he seemed to get a great deal of satisfaction from these statistics, as if he was in some way putting two fingers up to Westminster just by telling us.

Fifteen minutes had barely gone by before the telephone rang.

DUSTBINGATE!

All week we had had no calls and as soon as I was off work the bloody thing rings. I was silently cursing whoever it was on the other end when, before I had chance to pick it up, it stopped. As I was up now, I punched in last number redial. I did not recognise the telephone number, so I dialled it. 'Hello?' I was so surprised I nearly dropped the receiver. The voice was instantly recognisable to me but it was one I did not think I'd ever be hearing again.

The voice spoke again. 'Hello? Is someone there? Hello?'

I decided to answer.

'What the fuck do you want?' I put on my best friendly tone.

'All right, Ian?' came the reply. I could see his face in my mind's eye, all smiles and sincerity. He wanted something, I just knew it. How did he get my number? 'Christ almighty, you're a fucking bolt out of the blue, aren't you?'

'Yeah, it has been a while, hasn't it? Listen, Ian, don't be pissed off, mate, but I need a small favour.'

'Let me just interject there. Get fucked.'

The voice sighed. Here it comes, I thought.

'Oh, Ian, don't be like that!'

'Like what?'

I tried to feign disinterest, but he knew me – he knew I would be wondering what was going on. Why contact me now after all this time? Did he think I owed him some money? Was he feeling nostalgic for the 'good old days'?

'Will you meet me?' he asked. Obviously he had had it with pussy-footing around the matter.

'No.'

A pause, and then: 'Why not?' The tone of his voice had changed; now he was more business-like, more cool.

'Because all that – it's the past. You, the group, it's all over.' I replied.

'Come on, I want to have a chat, that's all.'

'Then chat. That's what phones are for.' I kept trying to figure out where he was going with this. My mind started to race – why was he phoning me? He knew he had me by the balls with this. My curiosity will be the death of me.

'When can you meet me? I need to see you, talk face to face.'

He was obviously trying to be as enigmatic as possible. 'Come on, Ian.'

'Look, I'm out of all that, I'm just not interested in it anymore.'

'It's very interesting, what I know. Please, meet me.'

Fucking hell, I thought, I've got a 'please' out of him. He must be desperate.

I saw my days off stretching in front of me full of sweet F.A., and I thought I might as well go to see the guy - after all, I would only be sitting on my arse all day. I stared at the clock. My partner would be home shortly. So much for a quiet day off.

'Where do you want to meet?' I asked.

The pleasure in his voice was obvious. 'How about the park?'

'When – today?'

'Erm, no. Today's out. How about tomorrow morning? Ten o'clock suit?'

I didn't seem to have much choice in the matter. 'OK, I'll see you then.'

The phone went dead. I shook my head. It was buzzing, part from tiredness, part in puzzlement. That phone call was a big shock to my system. A lot of memories came rushing back to me. One thing was clear though; when someone like that rings out of the blue, it can only mean that they want something – but what? I rubbed my stubble, four days worth. I supposed I'd better try to look human for this meeting, but I was not going to go on my own. I decided to make a phone call to a friend. A bit of back-up never goes amiss.

I was just about to make the call when I got my second shock of the day. My lady came home from work early. Here comes another big earful, I thought.

Oh yes, it was always good to get off nights and have nothing but total relaxation. She took one look at me and started.

'Oh, Ian! Haven't you got dressed yet?'

'I'm just going to get ready, love.' I smiled, but I knew she was full of it with me.

I ran up the stairs and into the shower. The call would have to wait, and even if he wasn't in, I decided I'd go alone if need be. I wanted to know exactly what was going on, and why a face from the past had decided to make me a part of it.

Chapter Three

That night I managed to call my friend Harry and ask him if he would come with me on my little sojourn to the park. He agreed, and I arranged to pick him up at nine the next morning.

Later, lying in bed, sleep was completely out of the question. I went back over and over the day's events. Christ, all I had wanted was a little peace and quiet on my days off and what did I get? Grief. First from Terry and then from my partner. She didn't know it was Terry on the phone – if she had known she would have hit the roof – in fact, she would probably have gone through the roof and clean out of the street. To her, Terry, and all he stood for, meant one thing – trouble.

There were three of us – Terry and Allen and myself. We created ourselves a union cell and we used to devise unusual and innovative ways of beating companies at their own game. Like some American unions, we wanted to use investigative methods to look into a company and their directors to see if, and more often, what illicit activities were going on.

We used methods that sometimes tended toward the bizarre, shall we say. It was all Allen's idea, and he would often quote an old Yorkshire saying to us: 'Where there's muck, there's money, and if you look close enough, where there's money, there's always muck.' This was his mantra and his justification for what we did, and he was usually right.

So we formed what we called the Direct Impact group and we had fun – a lot of fun. We were David, and they were Goliath. It wasn't exactly what you'd call a typical hobby, but we had a ball playing dirty tricks on fat-cat corporations, playing with their collective paranoid minds in the process. It beat darts, let me tell you.

There was no one set method or way of doing what we did,

but we had a philosophy, that there was always a way in – always. And we would find it, no matter how big or how bad the company, we would find its Achilles heel and we would make an impact.

We always made sure that no-one outside our little clique ever knew what we were up to, as secrecy was the primary concern. I used to imagine how good it would feel to have people coming up to me with a sly grin on their face, saying, 'What's all this I've been hearing about you, eh? You crafty little bastard!' The downside to keeping quiet is of course that you can never take the credit for anything that might come of whatever we did.

Listening to some union representative saying how he had done this and he had done that, when really he had done nothing at all really grates – but what were we going to do about it? Put up our hands and shout, 'Hey! Over here! We're the ones who did it! We're the ones who stirred the shit!' So we took satisfaction in knowing that we knew what we had done, even if no-one else did.

You have to remember one thing: The average working class bloke has a big mouth, and so we had to keep in the shadows. Sometimes, when something had to be brought into the open, all we had to do was say one thing to someone we knew who had an urge to mouth-off and half the job was done.

Say what you like, but the working class will fight and grass on each other in a heartbeat, believe me. The myth that they all stick together in solidarity against the tyranny of the ruling classes is bullshit. Average Joe Blow will shop his work mates for taking ten minutes too long on a tea-break, no question, so if it ever got out that we were scamming companies, we'd have been out of work like a shot.

Then, Allen died of a brain haemorrhage. It came out of the blue, and he was gone. I knew it wouldn't be the same again - I had lost my friend and my heart just wasn't in it anymore. And that was the end of that – or so I thought.

The next morning, I picked Harry up from his home at the pre-arranged time. Harry is a lot like me – always thinking.

I first met Harry about four years ago, when someone told me to ring him with regards to some information. He soon became a good friend, and was the only person outside the group who knew what we were up to. He knew Terry, which was why I wanted him to come along.

To be honest, I don't think he and Terry got along - at least, I was hoping that was the case. I wanted Terry to think that I was deliberately trying to intimidate him by bringing someone who would appear hostile and would be prepared, at a moments notice, to kick his teeth out on my say-so.

After Allen's death, Terry had all but vanished off the face of the earth. I sometimes wondered what had happened to him. I know what my lass would have liked to have happened to him – a long stroll off a short pier. He had met her just once, purely by accident. He came down to the house one afternoon and – surprise, surprise, 'Oh, hello love, you're home early. This is Terry.' She was kept out of everything to do with the group, but, as anyone in a relationship will tell you, just you try keeping secrets from them.

As soon as he had left, I got it. 'Ian, what the fuck's going on? What are you up to?' Whenever he rang, she would say: 'Ian, it's that twat for you.' Sometimes I kind of had the feeling that she knew something I didn't. Still, today I was about to catch up on old times.

'What does Terry want, then? All this time and not so much as a whisper – that fella's got to be up to something.' Harry wound down the window to let in some fresh air as I filled him in on the full details – I could only say so much over the phone.

I had always been a little uneasy about going into too much detail over the phone – you never knew who might be listening, and some of the things I said were a bit more contentious than most people's conversations. I did not want any unpleasant surprises knocking at my door.

Harry looked incredulously at me. 'You want me to basically sit and look menacing?'

'Yeah,' I said, 'make him think that any bullshit will be noticed and he'll be going back to wherever he's come from with two black eyes.'

'Ian, I'm not the action man type! I'm not gonna smack the guy just because he's running off at the mouth. He's probably just in the area and decided to look you up to have a bit of a brag, that's all.' I shook my head. 'No, no, no. I don't want you to actually get up and chin the fella – just look like you might.' I could see that he didn't like the idea, but it was required. I didn't think he was 'just in the area' – he was coming to me specifically because he wanted something. Arriving with someone was something he would not expect, and that was what I wanted – the edge.

We got to the park bang on ten to ten, and made our way through the old iron gates. It was cold that morning, and the place was deserted, except for the usual idiots who, rain or shine, walk their dogs so they can shit all over someone else's property instead of their own.

As we approached, I saw Terry sitting on one of the benches, looking in the opposite direction. He looked somehow different from how I remembered him. Harry spotted it immediately. 'Fuckin' hell,' he whispered to me as we got closer, 'has he won the lottery or summat? He looks like he's hit the jackpot!' Harry was right; as Terry rose to meet us, his outstretched hand had three rings on it. A knee-length coat, a three-piece suit! This was not the Terry I knew.

'Ian! How are you? Christ, four years, eh?' The grin was from ear to ear, but I noticed it shrank ever so slightly when he saw Harry. 'Hey! Harry, you look great. The pair of you, you both look great.' He motioned for us to sit down, so we did, Terry on one side, Harry on the other, and me in the middle.

Looking at him up close, I could see the differences in him, even in the way he spoke. 'Hey!' Like someone from a PR company – Mr 'can-do'. I could feel his eyes burning into me as he talked about the old days. He felt he had to sweet-talk me before asking for his favour. I decided to get the ball rolling myself and save the trips down memory lane.

'So what's up? Why all the cloak and dagger shit? Why ten in the morning?'

'Ian, I'm sorry about all this, but I work to a tight schedule, you know?'

'Fair enough', I replied, trying to sound interested. Harry shuffled in his seat, bored already.

'Well, get to the point, Terry, I'm freezing, we can't all afford winter coats.'

'Okay.' he had that workman-like tone to his voice again. 'What have you heard about World In Action sniffing around Hull?' This was not what I was expecting to hear, and by the look on my face I think Terry knew it. Only a few days ago at the factory I hear something like this, and now I've got people I haven't seen for years turning up and asking me all about it? I felt a strange feeling wash over me. Were these two events just a coincidence?

I kept quiet, and let Terry do the talking. He continued. 'Someone I know wants to know what, why and who. Will you, you know, do some digging?' He smiled.

I came out of my stupor and asked him, 'Why me?'

'You know why! You're good at delivering information – acquiring the facts.'

'Not anymore, Terry.'

'Why not?' he asked, straightening himself. He looked a wee bit pissed off at this.

'Because I can't be bothered, that's why!'

He glared at me. 'You have to! I said you would!'

'Oh yeah? Been throwing my name about, have you?' I dreaded him saying that; I've never liked the idea of people I don't know knowing all about me. Harry seemed to sense this, and stood up. He looked straight at Terry and gave him a grimace.

'Terry,' Harry said, not taking his eyes off him, 'have you been blabbing about the group? Because if you have, you'd better make sure that that coat you're wearing washes out blood. Ian and me's doing a big favour just being here.' I had to hand it to him, it was a great performance, and it seemed to do the trick.

Terry turned to me, suddenly less full of bravado. 'Ian, please just do a little snooping about. Not much, just a few phone calls here and there, you know the score.'

'I don't. Tell me.'

He sighed. So did Harry, who sat back down. 'All I know for sure is that a journalist from the programme World In Action is in town, or has been in town, and he's digging up stuff about local politics, or something that's going on. That's it, really.'

It was the same story that had been floating around the factory, no doubt about that. I thought for a moment. 'All right,' I said, 'I'll have a think about it. Where do I reach you?' He shook his head. 'No, I'll reach you. I know your number.'

'Just one thing, Terry. Why? Why you? Who are you working for? Why do you want this information?'

He stood, ready to leave. 'It's not important, Ian. Not now, anyway.' The conversation was over. Harry and I got up off the bench.

'See you later then.' He flipped up the collar of his coat and shook my hand.

He gave a cursory wave to Harry. Harry ignored him. The wind was beginning to bite, and I wanted to get going.

'You know what to do,' Terry half-whispered.

'If I feel like it,' I half-whispered back. Terry just grinned. He knew I would take the bait.

'I'm off,' he said, and indeed he was. We both stood and watched him disappear into the morning gloom.

'Well, what was all that about?' said Harry. 'I'm not sure, mate,' I answered, 'but you certainly put the shits up him. I thought you said you weren't the action man type? The poor bastard! I bet he thought you were gonna pull a fuckin' gun on him!'

Harry laughed. 'Well, he could have had a tank hidden in his! He looked like Arthur Daley in that fucker!' He pulled a face. 'I still don't know what he was going on about, though. Where does he work? Why ask you?'

'I don't know, but I'm doing fuck all for him. I might have a look around, but it'll be in my own time, and for myself.' This was turning surreal. Was something going on in Hull's political circle that people wanted to know about? World In Action, it seemed, thought there was. So did Terry and his bosses – whoever they were.

It was strange, but talking to Terry, I got the buzz I used to get when I would go after a company, a feeling of being alive. I had forgotten all about it until now, and now I had it back, I didn't want to lose it again. I decided I would ask around as there was obviously something to the story, but if Terry thought I was doing it for him, he was very much mistaken.

DUSTBINGATE!

Chapter Four

As we drove off, Harry seemed a little subdued. It had started to rain, and the inside of the car was close to freezing – what a day to pick for a 'chat' in the park. I asked him what was wrong.

Harry shrugged. 'I dunno, It's just him, the way he was acting, the way he was talking – he's certainly landed on his feet, hasn't he? I just don't trust him. I mean out of all the group, how come we all ended up on the bones of our arses while he came out on top?'

I knew what Harry was leading up to. A few years earlier several of us had got a knock on our doors out of the blue by the local Special Branch. All very friendly, if you know what I mean, but it was strange how Terry conveniently disappeared around then, while our fortunes went steadily downhill from there. We were not doing anything illegal you understand, but sometimes there are people in authority who find ideas more threatening than illegal activity. I suppose our little group might have fallen within that kind of 'threatening' category.

'I just don't trust the bastard.' Harry was emphatic.

There was no arguing with that. But I sensed that was not all that was bothering Harry. When someone you have not seen for a while turns up out of nowhere and looks, not like they used to, but instead like someone who had come into money, it can be a bit disconcerting – you can't help but wonder how they managed it.

You feel curious or jealous – whatever. But three things nag on the mind; that this person will not tell you who he is working for; secondly he is asking you to do something potentially very risky; and finally that he has been talking about you to his colleagues, you have a situation that is puzzling, if not downright worrying.

He knew me, and he knew Harry – and that is why Harry was

looking the way he did. The secret was out. How could I be sure that all those scams were not suddenly going to come back and haunt us? Harry had a hand in some, we all knew that, and we both had jobs to lose and people to answer to if it all blew up.

I was always aware of the risks involved, but you can't really understand those risks until there's a tap on your shoulder. I decided there and then that I would look into this, but not for Terry – for me. I was beginning to become extremely intrigued by all that I was hearing. Terry could disappear to wherever he lives now for all I cared – I would take what he told me and use it for myself.

There would be no further contact between Terry and me.

The rest of the journey back to Harry's house was quiet. We were both lost in thought following the morning's events and I knew Harry was not very happy about the whole thing.

Pulling up outside, I tried to put his mind at ease – but I couldn't, while my own was spinning.

I tried to change the subject. 'I meant to ask you, when are you changing to my shift?' He just looked at me. 'I'm not sure. Maybe in a couple of weeks, I think. Look, Ian...'

'It's all right. Trust me, he won't say or do anything. Forget today ever happened, okay?'

'Fair enough,' He replied, but I could see there was no chance of that happening.

He turned towards his house. 'I have to go, I'll see you later.'

I drove off, feeling bad. I had brought Harry along for a purpose – to intimidate, but in the end it was he who was left feeling intimidated. If I was going to look into this story – and I was still in two minds – then I would have to leave Harry out of things, at least for now.

Back at home, I sat down and had a think. If there actually was something shady going on in Hull, then how would one go about finding out? Gossip has to start somewhere, but beginning an investigation at a factory could lead to only one place – bullshit-land. I surmised that all the useful and accurate information I would hear from there I had already heard.

Picking up the phone, I dialled a local newspaper. I asked to be put through to one of their chief reporters, and to my surprise, I got straight through.

'Hello?'

'Yes, have you heard anything about a reporter from World In Action visiting Hull?' There was a pause. I continued.

'Do you know who he's been speaking to?'

'All we know is that he spoke to a few councillors a while ago, and that's it,' came the reply. 'May I ask who this is?' He sounded guarded, yet curious.

'Let's just say that we're both in the same business, and that I've been in the area, having a look around.'

'Oh, right.' I could sense he had taken the bait. If he would only give me something more than the stuff about the councillors.

'Can I have a name?' he asked.

'Stephen. That's all you need to know right now,' I said.

'Oh, okay. Are you working with' – and he gave me the reporter's name. I felt that this was all I would get from this partic-ular phone call, so I decided to wrap things up.

'I'll be in touch,' I said, and click, put down the receiver.

Voilà! Two pieces of info, and one seriously bemused journal-ist who would now be looking out for this 'Stephen' guy. To say I was happy with the way the conversation had panned out would have been putting it mildly. In just three or four minutes, I had found out that councillors had been involved in the reporter's investigation, and the reporter's name itself.

DUSTBINGATE!

I walked over to the window, and watched the rain. I love the rain, always have. As I stared out at nothing in particular, I went back in my mind to the mornings' little reunion. The mystery of it all had me thinking overtime; why the secrecy? Local politics was exactly that – local; as in small-time. Nothing big ever went on. What could possibly have happened that would necessitate all this interest?

I silently cursed the fact that in a couple of days I would be back at work.

The situation was surreal: here I was, getting involved in God-knows-what, meeting people in parks and ringing journalists pretending to be someone I'm not, and in less than forty-eight hours I'd be back on nights in a factory and buying dodgy tobacco.

What would be my next step? A voice in my head warned me to forget all about it, and although it had a point, I ignored it. I wondered whether I should sit on it until my next four days off? But that was unlikely; it was not as if my job demanded all my concentration. Our probe was going to occupy my mind now no matter how hard I tried to push it away.

Chapter Five

I was determined to make some serious leeway with all of this. World In Action was the obvious next port of call, but it would be a different ball game with them because these people knew what they were doing. They were not the local rag, whose typical front page was that a pensioner had mislaid his dentures or that somebody had nicked a charity collection box from a butcher.

Any telephone calls would be made from a local public phone box, I decided. That way nobody could trace any calls back to me, and equally importantly, my partner telling me to let the dog out would not interrupt any phone calls that were delicate or informative.

It was late evening by the time I had made up my mind to pursue this story, and because I worked nights, it was only now I really started to come alive. The trouble was that everyone else had finished for the day, and I hated having to wait around until the morning to act on all my ideas.

The next day I was up and about for nine, which was quite unusual for me. I had been awake most of the night, thinking about how to play it when I finally contacted World In Action. I figured I would simply ask if I could speak to the reporter at the centre of the investigation, and if that failed, I would attempt to contact the guy via other means. Perhaps a cryptic letter requesting a meeting; giving him just enough to whet the appetite, and make him wonder.

It was pissing down again as I stepped onto the street. I made sure I had my 'little book' with me. That book contained the phone numbers of everybody I had ever come into contact with during all my investigations. I had numbers of journalists, political organisations, businesses and – as luck would have it – several television production companies.

I entered the phone box. Usually, a line forms outside with

unbelievable speed. I did not need that, which was why I had started early. I had a quick look around to make sure there were not any unfamiliar faces hanging around or any cars parked that I did not recognise. Satisfied, I rang the operator and told her that I wanted to make a reverse charge call to Granada Television. I then said that I was a reporter from World In Action. By saying that I knew I'd get straight through.

I heard a click and then: 'Hello, can I help you?' It was a young woman's voice, very robotic, very well-mannered.

I tried to sound a bit more cultured than I am. I asked her if it would be possible to speak with the reporter who had been in Hull. I told her I had to speak with him urgently and that he would know what I meant.

She did as I might have figured and told me he was not there. But she assured me my message would get through, and that if I were to ring back after three that afternoon, I would reach him. So maybe she was telling the truth, and he really was out.

I thanked her and stepped out of the booth a fair bit happier. So far I hadn't experienced the big 'Fuck Off', that damn near impenetrable wall of silence that we sometimes hit when we were the Direct Impact group. It usually happened about halfway through an investigation into a company.

We would contact them and everyone we wanted to talk to was not available. In fact, they were never available. At first, paranoid bastards that we were, we used to think, 'Oh shit, somebody's rumbled us,' and we would steer clear. It was only after it had happened three or four times on the trot that we realised that companies, or, to be fair, the kinds of companies we were interested in, were populated by secretive, ignorant bastards.

Of course you can't really blame them. You cannot expect the secretary of Big Conglomerate PLC to beep one of its directors and say, 'Sir, it's some bloke you don't know from a hole in the wall wanting to talk to you about your private and most probably shady business dealings. Shall I put him through?'

I had six hours or so to kill before I could ring back, so I thought about what exactly I would say. I knew this World In Action reporter would be very guarded. Just getting the time of day out of the guy would be hard, never mind getting him to reveal what he was doing in Hull. There could be no messing around, as he would see right through any kind of clever, clever bullshit.

I trudged back home, soaking wet, watched the clock until it finally hit three o'clock, and then went back out to the phone box. I went over again how I anticipated the phone call might go. You talk to someone on the phone and sooner or later the 'X factor' will occur – the other person says something you did not expect, and the whole conversation is turned on its head. Before you know it, you're stuttering and stammering like an idiot, and you have to cut the call short and go away and rethink your whole battle plan.

'Hello, I rang earlier, is he back yet?'

The girl on the other end of the line remembered me, which made things a little easier. 'Oh, yes. One moment, please. I'll just put you through.' A click and then muzak in my ears. Just as it was coming to the chorus, there was another click, and I heard a man's voice. 'Can I help you? I understand you were trying to contact me earlier.'

He had obviously got my message. I began. 'Yes, we have been hearing all kinds of stories about someone from World In Action going up to Hull. Is that you?' A bit direct, maybe, but beating about the bush would get me nowhere. If he was going to dodge every question I asked anyway, I could at least take consolation in the fact that I went for the jugular. His answer was no surprise.

'I'm afraid I can't comment on that.'

'Fine,' I said, ignoring the coolness in his voice. 'Can I ask you, is there a programme being made in Hull?' Again, cool as ice: 'I can't comment, sorry.'

My mind was flying, desperately searching for a question that might knock him out of his automatic knee-jerk answers. Who in or from Hull could command such attention? There were only two people from Hull who were at all famous and, as far as I knew, Norman Collier wasn't up to anything. I quickly said something to get a reaction. (By the way, Norman Collier is a comedian, just in case you were wondering).

'Is it about John Prescott?' I asked, thinking back to the factory and the gossip from the shop floor.

'I think,' he said slowly, 'that you've just answered your own question, don't you?'

I went cold. I couldn't believe what I had just heard. After all the talk on the night shift and from Terry I had dismissed as bullshit, it seemed it was true that World In Action were in town trying to dig things up about the Deputy Prime Minster. I had to take a second to regain my composure.

'What are you looking into? I mean, it must be something pretty big...'

'Look,' he interrupted, 'I can't go into anything, okay?'

'Fair enough,' came my reply. I wanted to ask him more, but I knew that now was not the time for pushing my luck. I might need to get back in touch with this guy at a later date, and so annoying him was not a bright idea.

'Thank you for your time, I'll be in touch.' And with that I hung up.

As I opened the booth door, the cold wind seemed to hit me like a bullet.